1,001
TRIVIA
QUESTIONS

1,001
TRIVIA
QUESTIONS

Rick Campbell

Tommy Jenkins

William C. MacKay

FALL RIVER PRESS

New York

FALL RIVER PRESS

New York

An Imprint of Sterling Publishing
387 Park Avenue South
New York, NY 10016

Cover design by The Book Designers
Book design by Gavin Motnyk

ISBN 978-1-4351-4415-6

Distributed in Canada by Sterling Publishing
^c/o Canadian Manda Group, 165 Dufferin Street
Toronto, Ontario, Canada M6K 3H6
Distributed in the United Kingdom by GMC Distribution Services
Castle Place, 166 High Street, Lewes, East Sussex, England BN7 1XU
Distributed in Australia by Capricorn Link (Australia) Pty. Ltd.
P.O. Box 704, Windsor, NSW 2756, Australia

For information about custom editions, special sales, and premium and
corporate purchases, please contact Sterling Special Sales at 800-805-5489
or specialsales@sterlingpublishing.com.

Manufactured in the United States of America

2 4 6 8 10 9 7 5 3

· www.sterlingpublishing.com

The authors want to thank
Chris Barsanti, Maureen Slattery,
Sharon Bosley, and Mike Ferrari for
their encouragement and support.

1 Q:

How many Republican leaders led popularity polls in the two years before Mitt Romney clinched the 2012 nomination for president?

2 Q:

Name Barack Obama's three favorite films.

3 Q:

In what country and district does Katniss Everdeen reside?

4 Q:

What major effect has the enormously popular HBO series *Game of Thrones* had on one European country?

5 Q:

How did *Mad Men* viewers first learn that Don Draper was not the person he said he was?

6 Q:

Hundreds of years before the arrival of Columbus, the Anasazi, or Ancient Ones, established their own thriving culture in the Four Corners region of the American Southwest. What was the most spectacular accomplishment of these ancestral Puebloans?

1 A: Six candidates, according to *Slate*'s aggregation of major surveys from September 2010. In addition to Romney, the former frontrunners were Sarah Palin, Newt Gingrich, Herman Cain, Rick Perry, and Rick Santorum. Now, that's a horse race!

2 A: In a 2008 interview with Katie Couric, Obama cast his vote for *The Godfather*, *Lawrence of Arabia*, and *Casablanca*.

3 A: *The Hunger Game*'s heroic Katniss Everdeen lives in District 12 of the post-apocalyptic country of Panem.

4 A: Northern Ireland benefits not only from the direct spending of the award-winning fantasy show that shoots in their country, but also from the tourism that it inspires. In fact, one government official asserted that *Game of Thrones* will deliver the widest media exposure Northern Ireland has ever achieved outside of politics and the Troubles.

5 A: On a train bound for Manhattan, another passenger approached Draper, but called him Dick Whitman. Draper looked slightly shaken, but didn't correct him.

6 A: The Anasazi's masterfully planned and executed cliff dwellings are among the architectural wonders of the New World. Each year, millions of Americans visit Mesa Verde National Park to see them.

7 Q:
What happened to the Anasazi?

8 Q:
According to a 2002 study released by Hagerty Insurance
(an American classic-car insurer based in Michigan),
what is the single most dangerous food to consume
while driving?

9 Q:
What percentage of American households has two or
more vehicles?

10 Q:
What are the five most populous states?

11 Q:
Which five states have the lowest populations?

7 A: No one knows for certain. For decades, archaeologists and historians have been debating the causes of the sudden collapse of the Anasazi empire in the late thirteenth century. Theories have ranged from rapid climatic changes to disease to warfare and even cannibalism.

8 A: Not surprisingly, hot coffee tops the list of the ten most dangerous-while-driving foods. It is especially hazardous when consumed without a lid. Rounding out the list are hot soup, tacos, chili-covered food, juicy hamburgers, barbecue, fried chicken, jelly doughnuts, soft drinks, and chocolate.

9 A: According to a 2010 U.S. Census report, 57.5 percent of American households have at least two vehicles. In fact, almost 20 percent of households possess three vehicles or more.

10 A: California (37,253,956 population), Texas (25,145,561), New York (19,378,102), Florida (18,801,310), and Illinois (12,830,632) are the five states with the highest populations, as of the 2010 census. Pennsylvania is a close sixth, with 12,702,379 people.

11 A: As of April 1, 2010, the least populous states are, in ascending order: Wyoming (563,626), Vermont (625,741), North Dakota (672,591), Alaska (710,231), and South Dakota (814,180).

12 Q:
What did America's first vice president say about the office?

13 Q:
How many presidents were sons of presidents?

14 Q:
How many presidents have last names of only four letters?

15 Q:
How many presidents have had the first name of George?

16 Q:
Five presidents, present and past, attended Richard Nixon's funeral. Can you name them?

17 Q:
Who occupied the White House when a piano leg poked a hole through a first floor ceiling?

18 Q:
Besides Lyndon B. Johnson, which American presidents were born in the great state of Texas?

12 A: John Adams didn't much care for the job: "My country has in its wisdom contrived for me the most insignificant office that ever the invention of man contrived or his imagination conceived." John Adams later became the nation's second president.

13 A: Two. George W. Bush, our forty-third president, was the son of George H. W. Bush, chief executive number forty-one, and Founding Father and second president John Adams fathered John Quincy Adams, our sixth national leader.

14 A: Five. In addition to the two Bushes, there is a Taft (William H.), a Polk (James K.), and a Ford (Gerald).

15 A: Three. George Washington, George H. W. Bush, and George W. Bush.

16 A: At the historic May 1994 ceremonies, sitting chief executive Bill Clinton was joined by former presidents Gerald Ford, Jimmy Carter, Ronald Reagan, and George H. W. Bush.

17 A: Harry Truman. The Baldwin grand piano mishap became a wake-up call for executive mansion restoration.

18 A: Only one: Dwight D. Eisenhower. George H. W. Bush and George W. Bush were Texas residents when elected, but both were New England–born.

19 Q:
How many presidents arrived at the White House with a Ph.D.?

20 Q:
What fish is the world's largest?

21 Q:
What is the world's smallest fish?

22 Q:
What is the wingspan of the great horned owl?

23 Q:
What fish is the fastest swimmer?

19 A: Only one. Woodrow Wilson received his doctorate in political science from Johns Hopkins University in 1886, decades before he entered the Washington school of hard knocks.

20 A: The honor goes to the whale shark, which can grow longer than forty feet and weigh as much as 30,000 pounds. Despite its huge size, it is not considered a threat to humans. The whale shark is a filter feeder; it swims with its six-foot-wide mouth open, exposing its 600 tiny teeth, as it gathers small fish, crustaceans, and squid. The largest known whale shark was captured in 1919. It was over sixty feet long and weighed 80,000 pounds! That's a lot of filter feeding!

21 A: The tiniest fish discovered to date is the Sumatran *Paedocypris*, which is also the world's smallest vertebrate.

22 A: Great horned owls, the most common type of owl found in the Americas, have wings that can spread up to five feet wide.

23 A: Clocked at speeds of more than sixty miles per hour, the sailfish is considered the swiftest, though it is difficult to measure the exact speeds of fish.

24 Q:

What is the largest living animal on land or in the sea?

25 Q:

What is the largest land animal?

26 Q:

What are Gila monsters? Are they native to the United States?

27 Q:

Who invented the gasoline-powered automobile?

28 Q:

When was the Ford Motor Company founded?

24 A: The blue whale, which is eighty to ninety feet long, and has an average weight of 280,000 pounds. Its tongue alone weighs one ton! Not only is it the largest animal on earth, it is also the loudest. Blue whales emit low-frequency rumbling sounds that register louder than a jet engine or a heavy metal rock concert.

25 A: The African elephant. The world's largest land animal can weigh more than eight tons and measure twelve to thirteen feet tall. The Indian elephant is smaller, but still can weigh as much as six tons.

26 A: These large, venomous lizards are native to the Arizona deserts and the American Southwest. The Gila monster has a yellow and black tail and is eighteen inches long, with a stout body and a large head. Although it generally moves around slowly, it can bite suddenly and then hold on tenaciously to its victim.

27 A: Take your pick: Germans Karl Benz and Gottlieb Daimler are both credited with developing the internal combustion engine automobile, because they were the first to make commercially viable autos. Daimler developed a 1.5 horsepower, two-cylinder gas-powered engine in 1886, and Benz, working separately, developed a gas-powered car about the same time.

28 A: In 1903, Henry Ford organized and became the president of the company that bears his name. Ford had manufactured cars for several years before launching his own business.

29 Q:
In what year was General Motors founded?

30 Q:
In 1928, the Chrysler Corporation introduced the Plymouth as an inexpensive car to attract entry-level customers. When was the last Plymouth made?

31 Q:
Which car was the first to offer air-conditioning?

32 Q:
When was the first car theft?

33 Q:
What American-born man became prime minister and president of Ireland?

34 Q:
What American became prime minister of Israel?

35 Q:
How did Douglas "Wrong Way" Corrigan get his nickname?

29 A: The Olds Motor Company, the oldest unit of General Motors, was founded in 1897. When William Durant organized General Motors in 1908, it included the Buick Motor Company. In the next two years, it added Olds and Cadillac. By the 1920s, General Motors was the world's largest manufacturer.

30 A: The last car with the Plymouth marque was manufactured on June 28, 2001.

31 A: Packard exhibited an air-conditioned car at the Chicago Automobile Show in November 1939. The first fully automatic air conditioner was in the 1964 Cadillac.

32 A: Auto thievery started early. The first took place in June 1896, when a mechanic stole Baron de Zuylen's Peugeot.

33 A: New York City native Eamon de Valera.

34 A: Golda Meir. Israel's first female prime minister was born in Russia, but grew up in Milwaukee after her family emigrated to the U.S. in 1906.

35 A: On July 17, 1938, Douglas Corrigan filed a flight plan at New York's Floyd Bennett Field to fly to California, but somehow ended up in Dublin twenty-nine hours later.

36 Q:
What happened to Judge Crater?

37 Q:
In the sequence "2,3,5,7,11,13," what is the
next number?

38 Q:
What is litmus paper? What do its colors indicate?

39 Q:
What are the colors of the visible spectrum of light?

36 A: No one knows. On August 6, 1930, New York State Supreme Court Justice Joseph F. Crater disappeared. After telling friends that he was attending a Broadway play that evening, he removed papers from his files and cashed a check for a large sum. Late that afternoon, he was seen entering a taxi, but hasn't been sighted since. Ever since then, people have theorized about the cause of his disappearance: Was he involved in illegal activities? Was he murdered by the underworld? Did he run away? He was officially declared dead in July 1937, but we can still only speculate about why he vanished.

37 A: *The Big Bang Theory*'s Dr. Sheldon Cooper would know instantly: 17. These are, in ascending order, the lowest prime numbers. Prime numbers are numbers that cannot be divided by any number other than itself and 1.

38 A: Litmus paper is paper treated with a dye that measures the acidity and alkalinity of a solution, or its pH. If the paper turns red, it is acidic; if it turns blue, it is alkaline.

39 A: Red, orange, yellow, green, blue, indigo, and violet. Science students sometimes remember this sequence as "Roy G. Biv." Beyond the visible spectrum of light is ultraviolet, which is used in black lights, X-rays, infrared, and, most importantly, remote controls for televisions.

40 Q:
What are quasars?

41 Q:
When was the world's first artificial satellite launched?

42 Q:
This actor successfully escaped the Blob, but was unsuccessful in *The Great Escape*. Who was he?

43 Q:
In *The Cincinnati Kid,* the Kid takes on a stud-poker legend named Lancey Howard. Who played the aging card shark?

44 Q:
In *Breakfast at Tiffany's,* Holly Golightly must repeatedly visit a prisoner at Sing Sing and give him what?

45 Q:
Billy Wilder once said he was lucky enough to "catch" Audrey Hepburn twice. In what two films did he snare her?

46 Q:
Speaking of Billy Wilder favorites, the director made three movies with William Holden. Can you name them?

40 A: Although scientific debates about the nature of quasars still rage, it appears that they are stars moving away from Earth at great speeds, as shown by the red shifts in their spectra. They may also be distant galaxies.

41 A: The Soviet Union launched the communications satellite Sputnik into orbit on October 4, 1957. At the time, the United States could only counter by putting out several records with "sputnik" in the lyrics.

42 A: Steve McQueen.

43 A: Edward G. Robinson. The Kid was Steve McQueen.

44 A: The "weather report"; in actuality, coded messages for his drug ring.

45 A: *Sabrina* (1954) and *Love in the Afternoon* (1957).

46 A: *Sunset Boulevard* (1950), *Stalag 17* (1953), and *Sabrina* (1954).

47 Q:
Audrey Hepburn's debut starring role came in a film directed by William Wyler. Name the movie, her occupation, her leading man, and the most singular thing that happened to her because of the picture.

48 Q:
The Quarrymen included the nucleus of what well-known rock band?

49 Q:
What were The Who called before they became The Who?

50 Q:
Which member of the Grateful Dead inspired an ice cream flavor?

51 Q:
What is the name of the only Broadway show tune recorded by the Beatles?

52 Q:
How high can dolphins jump?

53 Q:
How fast can sea lions swim?

47 A: Hepburn played a princess in *Roman Holiday* (1953), co-starring Gregory Peck. She won the Oscar for Best Actress in her first starring role.

48 A: Future Beatles John Lennon, Paul McCartney, and George Harrison were all members of the Quarrymen. (Ringo Starr joined the Fab Four much later.)

49 A: Hang on: Pete Townshend and company were known as the Detours before they changed their moniker to The Who in 1964. Soon thereafter, however, these impetuous rockers became The High Numbers. After one very unsuccessful single, they realized their mistake and reverted to their now world-famous name.

50 A: Ben and Jerry's Cherry Garcia ice cream and frozen yogurt is named after the lead singer of the Grateful Dead, the late Jerry Garcia.

51 A: "'Til There Was You," from Meredith Wilson's *The Music Man*.

52 A: Dolphins can jump as high as twenty feet in the air. They can be seen accomplishing this feat at SeaWorlds and other parks around the world.

53 A: As fast as twenty-four miles per hour.

54 Q:
How much do giant pandas eat every day?

55 Q:
What was Seward's Folly?

56 Q:
In what year did Alaska become a state?

57 Q:
When and what was the Louisiana Purchase?

58 Q:
When did Lewis and Clark embark on their famous expedition?

59 Q:
When and where was Louis Armstrong born, and when and where did he die?

54 A: These large, lovable creatures consume as much as eighty-three pounds of bamboo a day and spend approximately twelve hours a day feeding. They are very picky eaters: They rarely eat anything other than fresh bamboo and turn up their cute panda noses up at frozen or freeze-dried products.

55 A: When the United States bought Alaska from Russia in 1867, the American press lambasted Secretary of State William Seward, who negotiated the deal for the "outrageous" $7,200,000 purchase price.

56 A: Alaska became the forty-ninth state of the United States in 1959. Hawaii joined the union the same year.

57 A: In 1803, Napoleon sold 827,987 square miles of the Louisiana Territory to the United States for $15 million. With that one purchase, the size of the nation doubled.

58 A: On May 14, 1804, Meriwether Lewis and William Clark left St. Louis to begin a transcontinental exploratory mission for President Thomas Jefferson. Their cross-country expedition took two and a half years.

59 A: Armstrong always claimed to have come into the world on July 4, 1900, but recently uncovered records indicate that he was born on August 4, 1901, in New Orleans. The incomparable jazz trumpeter and singer died in his sleep of a heart attack in New York City on July 6, 1971.

60 Q:

Louis Armstrong appeared in many films over the years. What was the last film he made?

61 Q:

Many musicians are best known by their nicknames. What were the birth names of these jazz legends: Dizzy Gillespie, Duke Ellington, Count Basie, Cannonball Adderley, and Fats Waller?

62 Q:

Invasion of the Body Snatchers (1956), *Flaming Star* (1960), and *Dirty Harry* (1971) were all directed by the same man, who had already won an Oscar for short subject direction. Can you name him?

63 Q:

Name the only movie that actor Charles Laughton ever directed. It's an offbeat flick, based on a Davis Grubb novel.

64 Q:

With thirty-million-dollar costs and low returns, *Heaven's Gate* (1980) earned infamy for sinking a distinguished movie production and distribution company. Identify the company, and also name the four early screen legends who launched this Hollywood giant.

60 A: Satchmo's last film was 1969's *Hello, Dolly!*, which was directed by Gene Kelly and stars Barbra Streisand. Louis, of course, sang the title song.

61 A: John Gillespie, Edward Kennedy Ellington, William Basie, Julian Adderley, and Thomas Waller.

62 A: Don Siegel.

63 A: *The Night of the Hunter* (1955), starring Robert Mitchum.

64 A: United Artists. Founded in 1919 by Mary Pickford, Douglas Fairbanks, Charlie Chaplin, and D. W. Griffith.

65 Q:

Joel Cairo, Bridgid O'Shaughnessy, and a guy named Wilmer are all key players in what classic 1940s movie?

66 Q:

In Huston's *The Maltese Falcon*, why does Sam Spade (Humphrey Bogart) insist that he's got to solve the murder of his partner Miles Archer (Jerome Cowan). Select the correct answer(s):

- a. As the dead man was his partner, he's expected to do something about it.
- b. If he doesn't, it'll be bad for business.
- c. Not only his partner, Spade was a devoted friend of Archer's.
- d. There's a reward for finding Archer's killer.

67 Q:

Married first to William Powell and then to Clark Gable, this gifted actress died in a plane crash in 1942. What was the name of the ill-fated starlet?

68 Q:

Which of these celebrities is not among Twitter's top ten most popular attractions: Taylor Swift, Britney Spears, Justin Bieber, Lady Gaga, Selena Gomez, Shakira, Kim Kardashian, Barack Obama, Rihanna, Oprah Winfrey.

65 A: *The Maltese Falcon* (1941), by first-time director John Huston.

66 A: Both **a** and **b**, but definitely not **c** and **d**.

67 A: Carole Lombard.

68 A: As of mid-2012, everyone except Oprah and Selena made that elite list.

69 Q:

What pint-sized Chilean-born reality star has more than five million followers on Facebook?

70 Q:

Which two *America's Next Top Model* winners were born outside the continental United States?

71 Q:

What popular musical variety show featured the Lennon Sisters? What were their first names?

72 Q:

How long was *The Lawrence Welk Show* on the air?

73 Q:

Bo and Luke Duke were two of the most popular television characters in the early '80s. Name the actors who played these two characters and the show in which they starred.

74 Q:

Who sang the theme song and also served as the narrator on *The Dukes of Hazzard*?

69 A: Nicole "Snooki" Pilozzi is just four foot nine, but she packs charisma that reverberates far beyond Seaside Heights, New Jersey, where *Jersey Shore* was filmed.

70 A: In May 2012, British-born Sophie Sumner surprised the world (and herself) when she became the winner of the eighteenth cycle of the WPIX show. Cycle eight top model Jaslene Gonzalez was born in Puerto Rico, but came to the mainland United States as a child.

71 A: Siblings Dianne, Janet, Kathy, and Peggy were the singing Lennon Sisters on *The Lawrence Welk Show*.

72 A: Beginning in 1955, Lawrence Welk hosted this ABC music fest for sixteen years; it was then syndicated for another eleven years. And believe it or not, it's still on the air: the reruns are being shown in syndication and on PBS.

73 A: Bo was played by John Schneider, and Luke was played by Tom Wopat on the CBS series *The Dukes of Hazzard*.

74 A: Waylon Jennings.

75 Q:

Denver Pyle played Uncle Jesse on *The Dukes of Hazzard*. On what other show did he have a recurring role as the head of the Darling family?

76 Q:

On *Laverne & Shirley*, Laverne had a very peculiar diet. What was her favorite drink?

77 Q:

Sticking with *Laverne & Shirley*, Shirley had a cherished stuffed toy cat. Can you name this fake furry feline?

78 Q:

"My name is Friday. I'm a cop." Who made these words famous and who played the character?

79 Q:

What is the literary significance of June 16, 1904?

80 Q:

Ernest Hemingway asserted that all modern American literature comes from one book. To which novel was Hemingway alluding?

75 A: Denver Pyle appeared in several episodes of *The Andy Griffith Show.*

76 A: Milk and Pepsi. The sitcom, which starred Penny Marshall and Cindy Williams, had a 178-episode, eight-year run that began in 1976.

77 A: Boo Boo Kitty.

78 A: Los Angeles police detective Sergeant Joe Friday demanded "just the facts, ma'am" from witnesses on *Dragnet* from 1951 to 1959. He was played by Jack Webb.

79 A: It's Bloomsday, the day in which all of the events of James Joyce's novel *Ulysses* occur.

80 A: Mark Twain's *The Adventures of Huckleberry Finn.*

81 Q:

"That's not writing; it's typing" was one famous writer's putdown of another's work. Who was talking about whom?

82 Q:

One famous American poet was a West Point cadet. Who was he and how did he fare?

83 Q:

One West Point graduate led a whole nation against the United States. Can you name him?

84 Q:

Recently the BBC touted a "two thousand-year-old computer." Is this for real or just media hype?

85 Q:

How did Confederate General "Stonewall" Jackson earn his nickname?

86 Q:

Which Civil War general popularized a new men's hairstyle?

81 A: Truman Capote's flip comment was made about Jack Kerouac's spontaneous prose style.

82 A: Edgar Allan Poe's brief stint at the United States Military Academy brought mixed results. In January 1831, after less than seven months there, he was court-martialed and dismissed. However, before he left, Poe convinced more than 130 of his classmates to subsidize the publication of his third book of poetry.

83 A: Jefferson Davis, the only president of the Confederacy, graduated from the United States Military Academy in 1828.

84 A: The Antikythera mechanism is the real deal. Recovered in 1901 from a shipwreck off a Greek island, this early first century BCE astronomical device qualifies as a real computer. With more than thirty interlocking gear wheels (and perhaps as many as seventy-two), the mechanism is a marvel of complexity and miniaturization, not to be replicated, as far as we know, for another fifteen centuries.

85 A: General Thomas Jonathan Jackson, also a West Point graduate, won his nickname at the First Battle of Bull Run (1861) the hard way, by holding his ground.

86 A: Union General Ambrose E. Burnside earned a niche in history for his mutton chops, which became known as "sideburns." He, too, graduated from West Point.

87 Q:

Which future presidents graduated from West Point?

88 Q:

How many future presidents graduated from Annapolis?

89 Q:

One American president was a former prisoner of war. Name him and the war.

90 Q:

Which state was the first to ratify the Constitution?

91 Q:

Which of the thirteen original states was the last to ratify the Constitution?

92 Q:

Name the first thirteen states of the United States.

93 Q:

Which eleven states seceded from the Union during the Civil War?

87 A: Ulysses S. Grant, class of 1843, and Dwight David Eisenhower, class of 1915, both earned diplomas from the United States Military Academy.

88 A: Only one. Jimmy Carter graduated from the United States Naval Academy in 1946.

89 A: Future Commander in Chief Andrew Jackson was just a teenager when he and his brother were captured by British troops during the Revolutionary War.

90 A: Delaware, which is still called the First State.

91 A: Initially opposed to joining the Union, Rhode Island became the last of the original thirteen states when it ratified the Constitution in 1790.

92 A: In the order of their statehood: Delaware, Pennsylvania, New Jersey, Georgia, Connecticut, Massachusetts, Maryland, South Carolina, New Hampshire, Virginia, New York, North Carolina, and Rhode Island.

93 A: South Carolina, Mississippi, Florida, Alabama, Georgia, Louisiana, Texas, Virginia, Arkansas, North Carolina, and Tennessee formed the Confederate States of America in 1861.

94 Q:
Twenty-three U.S. states are on seacoasts. How many can you name?

95 Q:
Name the six states that do not provide their governors with an official residence.

96 Q:
The capital city of a state is not always the largest city in the state. What are the capital cities of the following states: Kentucky, Wisconsin, Vermont, Pennsylvania, California, and Washington?

97 Q:
What American city boasts the longest continuous habitation by Europeans?

98 Q:
By now, all good trivia buffs know that George Washington never chopped down that famous cherry tree. Who told the lie?

99 Q:
What is the largest lake in the world?

94 A: Starting in the Northeast and going down the East Coast: Maine, New Hampshire, Massachusetts, Rhode Island, Connecticut, New York, New Jersey, Delaware, Maryland, Virginia, North Carolina, South Carolina, Georgia, and Florida. Continuing with Florida, and crossing the Gulf of Mexico: Alabama, Mississippi, Louisiana, and Texas. On the Pacific: Alaska, Washington, Oregon, California, and Hawaii.

95 A: Arizona, California, Idaho, Massachusetts, Rhode Island, and Vermont do not supply mansions for the governor. Fortunately, they do supply cars for the governors to get to work, though.

96 A: Frankfort, Kentucky; Madison, Wisconsin; Montpelier, Vermont; Harrisburg, Pennsylvania; Sacramento, California; and Olympia, Washington.

97 A: St. Augustine, Florida. Founded in 1565 by Spaniard Pedro Menendez, the settlement was established forty-two years before the English colonized Jamestown, Virginia.

98 A: To brighten his 1809 biography of the father of our country, Parson Mason Weems concocted the edifying fable of George Washington and his hatcheted cherry tree.

99 A: The Caspian Sea, with a surface area of 143,244 square miles. This salty lake borders five countries: Azerbaijan, Russia, Kazakhstan, Turkmenistan, and Iran.

100 Q:
What is the largest lake in North America?

101 Q:
List the Great Lakes in order of size.

102 Q:
Which Great Lake is the deepest?

103 Q:
Which of the Great Lakes does not border on Canada?

104 Q:
Who was the first woman elected to the House of Representatives?

105 Q:
When did women get the right to vote in U.S. national elections?

106 Q:
Where was the first women's rights convention held?

107 Q:
What was the first coeducational college in the United States?

100 A: Lake Superior, which is also the second-largest lake in the world. This vast body of water occupies 31,700 square miles.

101 A: From largest to smallest: Lakes Superior, Huron, Michigan, Erie, and Ontario.

102 A: The deepest of the five Great Lakes is Lake Superior. Its lowest point is 1,332 feet deep, theoretically almost enough to submerge the Willis (formerly named Sears) Tower.

103 A: Lake Michigan is wholly in the United States, bordering on Illinois, Wisconsin, Michigan, and Indiana.

104 A: Jeanette Rankin, Republican of Montana, became the first U.S. congresswoman in 1916.

105 A: The ratification of the Nineteenth Amendment on August 18, 1920, guaranteed women access to the ballot box.

106 A: Organized by Elizabeth Cady Stanton, the first Women's Rights Convention convened on July 19, 1848, in Seneca Falls, New York. A historic "Declaration of Sentiments and Resolutions" was issued at the convention.

107 A: Opened in 1833, Oberlin College admitted both men and women as students.

108 Q:

Who was the first woman sworn in as a Supreme Court Justice?

109 Q:

Which nation was the first to give women the right to vote?

110 Q:

When was the modern brassiere invented?

111 Q:

How were Wheaties invented?

112 Q:

When was soda first sold in a can?

113 Q:

In 1592, Pope Clement VIII famously endorsed a beverage. He had been petitioned by priests to ban this drink, but he refused. What beverage got his OK?

114 Q:

The Galapagos Islands belong to what country?

108 A: Sandra Day O'Connor took the oath in 1981.

109 A: New Zealand, in 1893.

110 A: Invented by New York socialite Mary Phelps Jacob, the first modern bra was awarded a patent in 1914.

111 A: Wheaties were discovered by accident in 1921, when a health clinician in Minneapolis, mixing a batch of bran gruel, spilled some on a hot stove. The gruel crackled into a crisp flake. Encouraged by the taste, he took the crisped gruel to the people at the Washburn Crosby Company, where the head miller, George Cormack, tested varieties of wheat before he developed the perfect flake. They introduced the cereal in 1924. In 1933, the advertising slogan "Wheaties—The Breakfast of Champions" was introduced.

112 A: The soda can was first developed in 1938 by the Continental Can Company for Clicquot Club ginger ale of Mills, Massachusetts. However, RC Cola was the first soft drink company to nationally distribute soda in cans in 1954.

113 A: Coffee. The pontiff reportedly rebuffed his advisors' attack on this "corrupting" beverage with the words, "This devil's drink is so delicious…We should cheat the devil by baptizing it."

114 A: These islands, located 500 miles off the Pacific coast of South America, comprise a province of Ecuador.

115 Q:
When did the Pillsbury Doughboy make his debut?

116 Q:
Who was Charles Sherwood Stratton? And how many people attended his wedding?

117 Q:
What does RSVP mean?

118 Q:
What is the common name for iron oxide?

119 Q:
Did the U.S. Navy ever research Frisbees?

120 Q:
Where was the Lost Colony and how did it get lost?

115 A: This advertising icon and mascot made his first appearance in advertisements in 1965. His formal name is "Poppin' Fresh."

116 A: Thanks to P. T. Barnum, the three-foot-four-inch-tall Stratton was known to millions as Tom Thumb. When he married Lavinia Warren, a woman of short stature, on February 10, 1863, more than 2,000 people attended the nuptials at Grace Episcopal Church in lower Manhattan. The couple was married for twenty years, until Stratton's death in 1883.

117 A: *Répondez, s'il vous plaît;* the French equivalent of "please respond."

118 A: Rust.

119 A: Yes, they did. In 1968, the Navy spent almost $400,000 in a study of Frisbees in wind tunnels, using cameras and computers. We are not sure what they learned, but we are certain it was important.

120 A: In 1587, English colonists reestablished a colony on Roanoke Island, although the island had been the site of an Indian massacre just the previous year. When Governor John White returned from an extended trip to England in 1590, he found the island deserted, dismantled, and perhaps plundered. Theories abound, but no one knows for sure what had happened to the 117 settlers.

121 Q:
Where was tobacco first grown?

122 Q:
Where was rice first grown?

123 Q:
On November 11, 1620, new colonists drew up and signed a 200-word declaration that has come to be regarded as a major document in American history. Can you identify this landmark agreement?

124 Q:
How many tentacles does an octopus have? How many tentacles does a squid have?

125 Q:
How many legs does a spider have? How many eyes?

121 A: The natives of the Americas used tobacco as far back as 2,000 years ago. Columbus brought the plant back to Spain, where its use spread throughout Europe.

122 A: We can't be certain, but it is believed that rice most likely originated in southern India, where it has been grown for thousands of years. From there, it spread eastward to China and the rest of Asia, and westward into Persia and Egypt. Rice was introduced to North America in the seventeenth century.

123 A: The Mayflower Compact. By signing the covenant, forty-one Plymouth settlers agreed to establish a "civil body politic," a government in their new home. Some historians regard the compact as the beginning of constitutional government in America. Others more cynically regard it as no more than a temporary document designed to avert a mutiny.

124 A: The octopus has eight tentacles. The squid has ten, two of which are specialized. The squid is no wimp—the giant squid is the largest creature on earth without a backbone, sometimes growing to fifty-five feet long and weighing two and a half tons.

125 A: All spiders have eight legs. Most have eight eyes, but some have only six. There are also spiders with two, four, and even twelve eyes.

126 Q:

Why do spiders seldom get caught in their own webs?

127 Q:

How fast can dragonflies fly?

128 Q:

Why do fireflies flash?

129 Q:

What educational first did W. E. B. DuBois attain?

130 Q:

Who were the Tuskegee Airmen?

131 Q:

What did Rosa Parks do on December 1, 1955?

132 Q:

When did Jackie Robinson become the first black baseball player in the modern major leagues?

126 A: These slippery creatures can get caught in webs, but it rarely happens. The tips of their legs are specially built, and the oil in their legs keeps them free-footed.

127 A: They can achieve speeds of up to thirty miles per hour.

128 A: A chemical reaction related to the mating process causes the bursts of light. The male and female fireflies have different patterns of flashing, but it is far too complicated and private to discuss here.

129 A: When he received his doctorate in 1895, William Edward Burghardt DuBois became the first African-American to receive a Ph.D. from Harvard.

130 A: The 332nd Fighter Group, known more popularly as the Tuskegee Airman, were the African-American graduates of the segregated pilot training program at Tuskegee, Alabama. In recent years, the long-ignored story of their valorous WWII service has become more well known.

131 A: On that day, she refused to give up her seat on a bus in Montgomery, Alabama. This act of bravery led to a boycott of Montgomery buses and was a major step in the battle for civil rights in the United States.

132 A: This Negro League star and future Hall of Famer joined the Brooklyn Dodgers in 1947.

133 Q:

Who was the first black Supreme Court justice?

134 Q:

Can you name the first African-American to win the Nobel Peace Prize?

135 Q:

Who invented the spinning jenny? What is it?

136 Q:

Match the inventors with their inventions.

Carrier	Machine gun
Babbage	Mercury thermometer
Nesmith	Air-conditioning
Birdseye	Correction fluid
Gatling	Frozen food (commercial)
Fahrenheit	Calculating machine

137 Q:

When was the zipper invented?

133 A: Thurgood Marshall was appointed by President Lyndon B. Johnson to the nation's highest court in 1967.

134 A: More than a decade before Martin Luther King Jr. won the honor, Ralph Bunche received the vaunted prize in 1950 for his work as a mediator in Palestine, while serving as the director of the United Nations Division of Trusteeship.

135 A: In 1764, Englishman James Hargreaves devised a hand-powered machine, which, by adding spindles to the spinning wheel, was able to spin numerous threads simultaneously. This innovation increased yarn production many times over. He named the machine for his daughter, Jenny.

136 A:
Carrier = Air-conditioning
Babbage = Calculating machine
Nesmith = Correction fluid
Birdseye = Frozen food
Gatling = Machine gun
Fahrenheit = Mercury thermometer

137 A: Whitcomb Judson, an engineer from Chicago, patented the first zipper in 1893, and exhibited it at the Chicago World's Fair that year. However, the new invention didn't catch on (so to speak) until B. F. Goodrich put zippers in his new product—rubber galoshes. Goodrich also coined the term: Until then, zippers were called "hookless fasteners."

138 Q:

In what year was the first Wright Brothers airplane flight?

139 Q:

All good trivia buffs know that Eli Whitney invented the cotton gin. But what is a cotton gin and why was the invention so important?

140 Q:

Among his elevated biographical film portrayals are Emile Zola, Louis Pasteur, and Benito Juarez—yet this actor rose to stardom playing a merciless killer. Name the actor and his breakthrough movie.

141 Q:

Make room for the moguls! Can you match the studio head with the studio he led?

Adolph Zukor............ **Universal**

Darryl Zanuck .... **Columbia**

Harry Cohn .... **Paramount**

Carl Laemmle .... **Twentieth Century-Fox**

138 A: 1903. In December of that year, Orville Wright piloted the first heavier-than-air, machine-powered flight in the history of the world. Although it lasted only twelve seconds, his 120-foot flight over the sandy dunes of Kitty Hawk, North Carolina, immortalized him and his brother Wilbur. A later flight that day went 852 feet.

139 A: Whitney's 1794 "engine" (or "gin") enabled plantation owners to separate the sticky green seeds from short-staple cotton fiber in an efficient and cost-effective way. Thanks to Whitney's invention, the yield of raw cotton in the South doubled each decade after 1800.

140 A: Paul Muni and the 1932 original of *Scarface*.

141 A:

Adolph Zukor = Paramount
Darryl Zanuck = Twentieth Century-Fox
Harry Cohn = Columbia
Carl Laemmle = Universal

142 Q:

Under their birth names, Joe Yule Jr. and Frances Gumm, they never became stars. But under their stage names (and thanks to MGM), they became the biggest box office duo in early-1940s musicals. Name them.

143 Q:

In this 1953 western, Jack Palance plays a sinister hired gun named Wilson. He's "terminated" by the title character of the film. Name the movie and the actor/terminator.

144 Q:

Why are oil, gas, and coal called fossil fuels?

145 Q:

Where is the largest oil field in the world?

146 Q:

How many gallons are in a barrel of oil?

147 Q:

Where was oil first discovered in the United States?

148 Q:

What does OPEC stand for?

142 A: Mickey Rooney and Judy Garland.

143 A: *Shane*, starring Alan Ladd.

144 A: Because they are composed of the remains of organisms that lived long ago. Over the course of millions of years, these organisms decompose and are converted into fuel.

145 A: The largest oil field in the world is the Ghawar field in Saudi Arabia.

146 A: The barrel, a standard measure of crude oil, contains forty-two U.S. gallons.

147 A: The first oil well in the United States was drilled in Titusville, Pennsylvania, by Colonel Edwin L. Drake in August 1859.

148 A: The Organization of Petroleum-Exporting Countries.

149 Q:
What is a yak?

150 Q:
Where are pandas found in the wild?

151 Q:
Are pandas bears?

152 Q:
What animal is the world's tallest creature?

153 Q:
What is the largest living rodent?

149 A: This large, long-haired ox is native to the high plateaus and mountains of Tibet, where the climate is cold and dry. The males are more than six feet high at the shoulder and weigh more than one ton. The wild yak, which is larger than the domesticated yak, is considered to be an endangered species.

150 A: In the wild, these giant quirky creatures are found only in three provinces of China: the Sichuan, Gansu, and Shaanxi. Though their habitat once covered as much as 300,000 square miles, these migrating animals now live within an 83,000-square-mile territory.

151 A: Yes. For decades, this was a matter of dispute, but recent molecular research indicates that the giant panda is indeed a true bear.

152 A: The male giraffe, which averages seventeen feet in height.

153 A: The capybara. This semi-aquatic rodent measures about two feet tall at the shoulder, and can weigh more than one hundred pounds. Capybaras are shorthaired, brownish rodents, with blunt snouts, short legs, small ears, and almost no tail. South American capybaras can be up to four feet long; Panamanian capybaras are a little smaller. They are vegetarians, and like to eat from people's gardens.

154 Q:
At the time of the arrival of the Europeans, what was the range of the American bison in North America?

155 Q:
What was the name of the Ewings' ranch on the TV show *Dallas*?

156 Q:
Which actors played the following TV doctors: Dr. Kildare? Ben Casey? Dr. Ross on *ER*?

157 Q:
Warren Beatty appeared as a regular on what popular 1950s sitcom?

158 Q:
Who was the narrator on the 1950s television series *The Untouchables*?

159 Q:
The Honeymooners (1952–57) centered around Jackie Gleason's Ralph Kramden. Why did Ralph wear a uniform?

154 A: The American bison, commonly known as the buffalo, once roamed North America coast to coast, all the way from the West to the Eastern Seaboard. The herd population was estimated to be as high as fifty million animals. By 1900, there were fewer than 1,500 bison left.

155 A: South Fork.

156 A: They were played, respectively, by Richard Chamberlain, Vince Edwards, and George Clooney.

157 A: In the 1959–60 season of *The Many Loves of Dobie Gillis*, Beatty played Milton Armitage, Dobie's rich rival for the affections of the beguiling Thalia Menninger, who was portrayed by Tuesday Weld.

158 A: Walter Winchell. The famed newspaper gossip columnist received $25,000 to narrate each episode of this weekly drama. On this partially fact-based show, machine-gun-wielding gangbuster Eliot Ness (portrayed by Robert Stack) tracked down assorted real-life mobsters, such as Frank Nitti (played by Bruce Gordon). The show, which aired from 1959 to 1963, was among the most violent—and popular—shows of its time.

159 A: When Kramden wasn't dressing up in Raccoon Lodge regalia, he was donning the uniform of the Gotham Bus Company.

160 Q:

Where did Ralph's wisecracking sidekick Ed Norton work?

161 Q:

Where did Ralph, Alice, Ed, and Trixie live?

162 Q:

Every Tuesday, *The Honeymooners'* Ralph Kramden plays pool; every Thursday, he bowls. What does Ralphie Boy do on Friday nights?

163 Q:

What was the name of the character played by Ted Danson on the television comedy *Cheers* (1982–93)? What was the name of his longtime girlfriend, who was played by Shelley Long?

164 Q:

What was Indiana Jones's first name?

165 Q:

What's the name of the movie star character Gene Kelly plays in the 1952 musical *Singin' in the Rain*? How about the name of his glamorous silent-screen leading lady?

160 A: Underground. He was a New York City sewer worker.

161 A: In an apartment building on Chauncey Street, in the Bensonhurst section of Brooklyn.

162 A: Attend the meetings at the Raccoon Lodge, of course.

163 A: Sam Malone and Diane Chambers. The former Boston Red Sox player pursued Diane for the show's first five seasons.

164 A: Henry.

165 A: Kelly plays Don Lockwood; actress Jean Hagen plays Lina Lamont.

166 Q:

In *Singin' in the Rain,* what's the name of the studio where the characters played by Gene Kelly and Donald O'Connor work?

167 Q:

Another *Singin' in the Rain* question: Gene Kelly's character gets his first big break in the movie business by doing what?

168 Q:

One of the most famous scenes in movie history is Gene Kelly's dancing through a downpour while singing the title song of *Singin' in the Rain.* Name the types of stores Kelly passes while performing this number.

169 Q:

Where are the Weddell and Ross Seas?

170 Q:

Who was the first person to reach the South Pole?

171 Q:

Who was the first to fly over the South Pole?

166 A: Monumental Pictures.

167 A: Working as a stuntman.

168 A: A women's clothing store, a drugstore, a music studio, a millinery shop, a bookstore, and the Mount Hollywood Art School.

169 A: Antarctica.

170 A: The Norwegian explorer Roald Amundsen on December 13, 1911.

171 A: Richard E. Byrd. The American admiral made aviation history when he flew his tri-motor plane across the southern pole.

172 Q:

What percentage of the world's freshwater is in the frozen ice mass of Antarctica?

173 Q:

Who bites more frequently: male or female mosquitoes?

174 Q:

One basketball team won eight consecutive NBA championships. What team and in which years?

175 Q:

Only one NBA player has ever averaged fifty points a game for a complete season. Who was it?

176 Q:

How many seasons did the American Basketball Association survive?

177 Q:

Who holds the record for most lifetime points in the NBA?

178 Q:

What team has won the most NCAA championships in men's basketball?

172 A: 70 percent.

173 A: Male mosquitoes do not bite humans. Instead, these little vegetarians live on plant sap and juices.

174 A: The Boston Celtics won National Basketball Association titles every year from 1959 through 1966.

175 A: Wilt Chamberlain. During the 1961–62 NBA season, the Philadelphia 76ers center averaged an incredible 50.4 points per game. On March 2, 1962, in a game against New York, he scored 100 points.

176 A: Nine seasons, from 1967 to 1976. After the league ceased operations, four ABA teams joined the National Basketball Association: Indiana, Denver, San Antonio, and the New York Nets.

177 A: Kareem Abdul Jabbar. During his career, the former Lew Alcindor scored 38,387 points.

178 A: UCLA has triumphed in eleven NCAA championships. The University of Kentucky is second, having won the crown seven times.

179 Q:
The Basketball Hall of Fame gives out the Chip Hilton Award and the Clair Bee Award each year to the nation's outstanding college player and outstanding coach. For whom are they named?

180 Q:
Dr. Richard Mudd, who died in 2002, spent seven decades trying to clear the name of Dr. Samuel Mudd, his grandfather. Who was the older Dr. Mudd, and for what crime was he convicted?

181 Q:
Was the fictional character of Sherlock Holmes based on a real person?

182 Q:
When did Alfred E. Neuman first appear in *MAD* magazine?

179 A: Clair Bee (1896–1983) was a basketball coach at Rider and Long Island Universities from 1929 to 1951, compiling an impressive record of 412 wins and 87 losses. In his spare time, Bee authored twenty-four Chip Hilton novels, which were published from 1948–66. The Chip Hilton novels told of sports heroics by the title character and his teammates.

180 A: This Maryland physician was one of eight people convicted of conspiracy in the assassination of President Abraham Lincoln. Soon after the assassination, Mudd set John Wilkes Booth's broken leg and allowed him to rest in his home for several hours.

181 A: Dr. Joseph Bell inspired the Baker Street genius detective. In 1877, when Arthur Conan Doyle was studying to be a doctor, Bell was one of his professors. Like Holmes, Dr. Bell had excellent deductive abilities when observing people.

182 A: With his jug ears and missing tooth, the MAD mascot made his first comic book appearance in a tiny picture in February 1955's issue #21. He had previously showed up on the cover of the November 1954 paperback, *The MAD Reader*.

183 Q:

Match the comic strips with their creators.

Doonesbury. . . . . Chester Gould
Dick Tracy . . . . .Gary Larson
Peanuts . . . . Walt Kelly
Pogo . . . . .Charles M. Schulz
Far Side. . . . . Garry Trudeau

184 Q:

In what year was gold first discovered in California's Sutter's Mill?

185 Q:

When did Mrs. O'Leary's cow cause the Chicago Fire?

186 Q:

When did the Great San Francisco Earthquake strike?

187 Q:

Before they became famous, singers James Brown, Dean Martin, and Jackie Wilson all participated in what sport?

188 Q:

Who were the songwriters for many of Jackie Wilson's early records, including his first hit, "Reet Petite"?

183 A:
Doonesbury = Garry Trudeau
Dick Tracy = Chester Gould
Peanuts = Charles M. Schulz
Pogo = Walt Kelly
Far Side = Gary Larson

184 A: 1848. On January 24 of that year, James Marshall panned the first gold nuggets there. By 1849, 80,000 prospectors had arrived in the territory. Within a few years, more than 500,000 people had migrated to California.

185 A: The great Windy City conflagration began on October 8, 1871, but to this day it is unclear how it started. Mrs. O'Leary's bovine became the fall guy (cow).

186 A: On April 18, 1906, San Francisco suffered its worst seismic upheaval. This quake and the fires and aftershocks that followed left 503 dead and caused $350 million in damages.

187 A: In their youth, all three were amateur boxers. Jackie Wilson was even a Golden Gloves Champion in Detroit. Dean Martin boxed under the name of Kid Crochet.

188 A: Berry Gordy Jr. and Tyron Carlo. Gordy went on to found Motown Records.

189 Q:

Where was the original recording studio for Motown Records?

190 Q:

What was the title of the first hit record by James Brown and the Famous Flames?

191 Q:

What was the name of Dean Martin's partner in a popular song and comedy act?

192 Q:

Which river is the longest in the world?

193 Q:

Which lake is the largest in Africa?

194 Q:

What countries does the Nile pass through on its way to the Mediterranean Sea?

195 Q:

What is the longest river in the United States?

189 A: In Detroit at 2648 West Grand Boulevard. "Hitsville USA" was the name given to this studio, where many of the first Motown hits were recorded.

190 A: *Please, Please, Please*, originally released on Federal Records in 1956, wasn't just their first hit; it was their first record.

191 A: Jerry Lewis. Martin and Lewis were a popular team in the 1950s, making numerous movie, television, and radio appearances together.

192 A: The longest is the Nile in Africa, which flows 4,160 miles to the Mediterranean Sea. The next two longest rivers in length are the Amazon and the Chang Jiang (Yangtze) Rivers.

193 A: Lake Victoria, one of the sources of the Nile, is the largest lake on the continent. Its 28,820 square miles make it the third-largest lake in the world.

194 A: The basin of the world's longest river includes Burundi, Rwanda, Tanzania, Kenya, Uganda, Congo, Sudan, Ethiopia, and Egypt.

195 A: There are two possible answers: The Mississippi River, which flows 2,340 miles from Lake Itasca, Minnesota, to the Gulf of Mexico, is the longest river in the U.S.; or the Mississippi-Missouri-Red Rock River system, which runs 3,710 miles from Montana to the Gulf of Mexico.

196 Q:
The Mississippi River forms one of the borderlines of ten different states on its voyage from its source in Minnesota down to the Gulf of Mexico. Can you name the states?

197 Q:
List the oceans in order of size.

198 Q:
Is it possible to drown in the Dead Sea?

199 Q:
Barack Obama, Bill Clinton, George H. W. Bush, Herbert Hoover, Ronald Reagan, James Garfield, and Gerald Ford share one thing in common. What is it?

200 Q:
Which president could write Latin with one hand and Greek with the other?

201 Q:
What was the birth name of Billy the Kid? Who shot him?

202 Q:
How did Jesse James die?

196 A: After splitting the twin cities of Minneapolis and St. Paul, the Mississippi forms parts of the borderline of the states of Minnesota, Wisconsin, Iowa, Illinois, Missouri, Kentucky, Tennessee, Arkansas, Mississippi, and Louisiana. It empties into the Gulf of Mexico.

197 A: From the largest to the smallest: the Pacific, Atlantic, Indian, and Arctic oceans.

198 A: Yes, but not very easily: The high salt content of the Dead Sea causes one to float effortlessly.

199 A: Each of them wrote left-handed.

200 A: James A. Garfield.

201 A: William "Billy the Kid" Bonney was born Henry McCarty in 1859. On July 14, 1881, he was shot to death by Sheriff Pat Garrett in New Mexico.

202 A: On April 3, 1882, while he was straightening a picture on a wall, James was shot in the back of the head by Robert Ford. Thereafter, Ford was known as "that dirty little coward who shot Mr. Howard"—Howard being Jesse James's last known alias.

203 Q:
Who fought at the OK Corral on October 26, 1881?

204 Q:
What was Annie Oakley's birth name?

205 Q:
Who invented the Bowie knife?

206 Q:
Who created the metric system?

207 Q:
When was the first running of the Kentucky Derby?

208 Q:
Who else was shot during the assassination of President John F. Kennedy on November 22, 1963?

203 A: As every cowboy moviegoer knows, the Earp Brothers and Doc Holliday exchanged gunfire with the outlaw Clanton Gang and the McLaury brothers. For added firepower, Virgil Earp, the sheriff of Tombstone, Arizona, had deputized his brothers Wyatt and Morgan.

204 A: Phoebe Anne Moses. Although she never lived farther west than Ohio, Annie Oakley won well-deserved fame as an expert rifle and shotgun marksman in Buffalo Bill's Wild West show.

205 A: It is believed that Rezin Bowie invented the Bowie knife; however, it was his brother Jim Bowie who popularized it.

206 A: Now used in most countries of the world, the French Academy of Sciences devised the metric system in the late eighteenth century to replace the noncompatible measuring systems then in use. The scientists' goal was to standardize the measurements and to use the decimal system rather than fractions.

207 A: Organized by Colonel Meriwether Lewis Clark Jr., the first Kentucky Derby was run in Louisville on May 17, 1875.

208 A: Texas Governor John Connally was seriously wounded while riding in the presidential procession in Dallas.

209 Q:
When was the first Woolworth's store opened?

210 Q:
When did Sears, Roebuck and Co. begin?

211 Q:
Where did J. C. Penney originate?

212 Q:
Barnes & Noble was founded in what year?

213 Q:
Which country has the largest population?

214 Q:
Which country has the smallest population?

215 Q:
In which country do people speak Esperanto?

216 Q:
What do Istanbul, Constantinople, and Byzantium have in common?

209 A: Frank W. Woolworth opened the first five-and-dime store in Utica, New York, on February 22, 1879. The last Woolworth's store closed in 1997.

210 A: A year after starting in Minneapolis in 1886, the R. W. Sears Watch Company moved to Chicago, where they hired a Mr. Roebuck as a watchmaker. In 1893, Sears, Roebuck and Co. was formed and began to issue the first of its famous catalogs.

211 A: In 1902, James Cash Penney opened his first store in Kemmerer, Wyoming.

212 A: In 1873, Mr. Barnes formed a bookselling organization in Wheaton, Illinois. He moved the company and joined up with Mr. Noble in New York City a few years later.

213 A: China, with an estimated 1.3 billion people. India has the second-largest population, with more than 1.2 billion inhabitants.

214 A: The one-half-square-mile Vatican city-state, which has approximately 800 residents.

215 A: Nowhere. It is an artificial international language, which never became accepted.

216 A: They are three historical names for the same city: present-day Istanbul.

217 Q:
What historic event occurred on July 14, 1789?

218 Q:
What happened on June 28, 1914?

219 Q:
When did World War II begin?

220 Q:
When was the Berlin Wall built? When did it come down?

221 Q:
How many people died in the flu epidemic of 1918–19?

217 A: On that day, an angry French crowd stormed Paris's Bastille, a fortress used as a prison. July 14 is now commemorated in France as Bastille Day.

218 A: On June 28, 1914, a Serbian activist assassinated Archduke Francis Ferdinand, the heir to the throne of Austria-Hungary, and his wife, in Sarajevo. Within two months, tensions had escalated into the First World War.

219 A: The actual fighting began when German troops crossed the border into Poland on September 1, 1939. Pledged to support Poland, Britain and France declared war on Germany two days later. The United States did not enter the war until December 1941.

220 A: The Berlin Wall was constructed in August 1961 to stop escapes by East Germans to West Berlin. The wall was dismantled in 1989.

221 A: In the three waves of the 1918–19 "Spanish Flu," at least twenty million people succumbed. Indeed, many estimates run as high as thirty million dead. Coming on the heels of the First World War (in which ten million perished), the pandemic spread more quickly and widely because of the large troop movements of the time.

222 Q:

When did the first drive-in movie theater open?

223 Q:

In a 1988 movie, Sally Field and Tom Hanks were paired as potential lovers. Only a few years later, in 1994, Field played Hanks's mother. Name these two films.

224 Q:

Name the presidents whom Forrest Gump meets.

225 Q:

Who was the actor who played Staff Sgt. Raymond Shaw in *The Manchurian Candidate*? What is the name of the actress who played his "cool as a cucumber" mother?

226 Q:

What was the actual age difference between the actor playing Staff Sgt. Shaw and his screen mother in *The Manchurian Candidate*?

227 Q:

Although *The Matrix* takes place in a fictional city, the street names can all be found in what American city?

222 A: Richard Hollingshead opened a drive-in movie theater in Camden, New Jersey, on June 6, 1933. He hoped it would be enough of an attraction to boost sales at his gas station. It was sold out the first night (the first film shown was *Wife Beware*) and for many nights after that.

223 A: *Punchline* (1988) and *Forrest Gump* (1994).

224 A: John F. Kennedy, Lyndon Johnson, and Richard Nixon.

225 A: Laurence Harvey. Angela Lansbury played his mother in the 1962 film.

226 A: Angela Lansbury was three years older than Laurence Harvey.

227 A: Chicago, which is the hometown of writers/directors Larry and Andy Wachowski.

228 Q:

Who played the character Liz Teel in the unrelated 1993 television series *The Matrix*?

229 Q:

On *Friends,* Joey Tribbiani got a big break in his career when he was cast on a soap opera. Unfortunately, his character died in a tragic accident. What soap was he on? How did his character meet his death?

230 Q:

What movie star invented a radio-controlled torpedo?

231 Q:

In the 1950s, psychologist Dr. Joyce Brothers won the big prize on *The $64,000 Question.* In what subject did she compete?

232 Q:

Who was the only heavyweight boxing champion to end his career undefeated?

233 Q:

When did Joe Louis first become the heavyweight champion?

228 A: Carrie-Anne Moss, who also plays Trinity in the film *The Matrix*.

229 A: *Days of Our Lives.* After Joey insulted the show's writers, they had his character, Dr. Drake Ramoray, fall down an elevator shaft.

230 A: Hedy Lamarr, who was born in Austria as Hedwig Eva Kiesler, was both a film star and an inventor. She starred in several MGM films, including *Algiers* (1938) and *White Cargo* (1942), but she also was granted a patent for a radio-controlled torpedo. The technology she invented was later used in satellite technology.

231 A: Dr. Joyce Brothers's area of expertise was boxing.

232 A: When he retired from boxing in 1956, heavyweight champion Rocky Marciano had a professional record of forty-nine victories and no defeats or draws. He had held the world championship for four years.

233 A: On June 22, 1937, Joe Louis, also known as the "Brown Bomber," knocked out James J. Braddock, thus beginning his twelve-year reign as the world heavyweight champion.

234 Q:
Who was nicknamed the "Manassa Mauler"?

235 Q:
What fight was known as the "Thrilla in Manila"?

236 Q:
What was James Cagney's first film?

237 Q:
What was the last film in which James Cagney appeared?

238 Q:
What drama series starred an ex-wife of the president of the United States? The plot revolved around family disputes over the control of a vineyard.

239 Q:
Annette Funicello made her television debut on what afternoon show?

240 Q:
What former Mouseketeer played Jeff Stone on *The Donna Reed Show* (1958–66)?

234 A: Jack Dempsey. The former barroom bouncer earned his nickname partly because he had born in Manassa, Colorado.

235 A: The aptly named Muhammad Ali–Joe Frazier championship fight in 1975. Ali won the hard-fought match when Frazier was unable to come out for the fifteenth round.

236 A: His first film was *Sinner's Holiday*, which was released in 1930. He had played the same part in the 1929 Broadway show.

237 A: *Ragtime*, in which he played Police Chief Rheinlander Waldo, was released in 1981. He was also in a 1984 television movie titled *Terrible Joe Moran*, in which he teamed up with Art Carney. Cagney died in 1986.

238 A: Among the stars of *Falcon Crest*, which debuted in 1981, was Jane Wyman, who was once married to Ronald Reagan. She played matriarch Angela Channing.

239 A: Annette was a Mouseketeer on the original daily afternoon *Mickey Mouse Club* (1955–59).

240 A: Paul Peterson played the son of Donna Reed and Carl Betz on that classic family sitcom of the late 1950s. Shelley Fabares played his sister, Mary.

241 Q:

What future sitcom star had a short-lived role on the 1980s series *Benson*?

242 Q:

In which city was the first electric traffic light installed?

243 Q:

What is the date of the Magna Carta?

244 Q:

Who fought in the Hundred Years War? Did it really last one hundred years?

245 Q:

When did Marco Polo go to China?

246 Q:

What are the names of the wives of Henry the Eighth?

241 A: Jerry Seinfeld played Frankie on the sitcom, which starred Robert Guillaume as the title character.

242 A: Cleveland, Ohio. When Garrett Morgan installed his device on the corner of East Euclid and East 105th Street, no other city in the world had an electric traffic signal. Morgan, the son of a freed slave, can be credited also with another life-saving invention: the gas mask.

243 A: King John of England signed the 1215 document, which guaranteed the privileges of nobles and church against the monarchy, and also assured the right to a jury trial.

244 A: France and England were officially at war from 1334 to 1453, but they fought few battles during much of that time. It was not until 1565 that the English were forced out of Calais, their last foothold on the French mainland.

245 A: In 1260, Marco Polo, son of a Venetian merchant and explorer, accompanied his father on an overland journey to China. His record of his Asian adventures, written while he was imprisoned, became the most famous travel book in history.

246 A: Henry VIII, who ruled England from 1509 to 1547, married six times. His not-always-so-lucky wives were Catherine of Aragon, whom he divorced; Anne Boleyn, whom he beheaded; Jane Seymour, who died during childbirth; Anne of Cleves, divorced; Catherine Howard, another decapitation; and Catherine Parr, who, somehow, outlived him.

247 Q:
How many of the Allman Brothers were actually brothers?

248 Q:
How were the Beach Boys related?

249 Q:
What was the relationship between Gladys Knight and the Pips?

250 Q:
How are the Bee Gees related?

251 Q:
Where did the Doobie Brothers get their name?

252 Q:
What were the names of the identical cousins on *The Patty Duke Show* (1963–66)?

253 Q:
What are the names of the nephews of Donald Duck?

254 Q:
What is Scrooge McDuck's relationship to Donald Duck?

247 A: Two: Duane and Gregg.

248 A: Three of the original Beach Boys were brothers—Brian, Carl, and Dennis Wilson. One, Mike Love, was a cousin, and the other, Al Jardine, was a neighbor.

249 A: Gladys's back-up singers, the Pips, consist of two of her cousins, and her brother, Merald, also known as "Bubba."

250 A: Robin, Barry, and Maurice Gibb are brothers.

251 A: A "doobie" is slang for a marijuana cigarette. They are not actually blood relations.

252 A: Patty Lane and Cathy Lane, both played by Patty Duke.

253 A: Huey, Dewey, and Louie.

254 A: Scrooge McDuck is Donald's billionaire uncle. He is believed to be the brother of Donald's mother.

255 Q:

Sha Na Na, who first made it big in 1969, was a singing group composed of undergraduate students from Columbia University performing versions of '50s doo-wop songs. Where did they get the name "Sha Na Na"?

256 Q:

When was "The Star-Spangled Banner" written? What inspired its author to write it?

257 Q:

What is the Monroe Doctrine?

258 Q:

What happened at the Alamo in early 1836?

259 Q:

When did the Erie Canal open?

260 Q:

Which bird is the fastest flyer?

255 A: The group's name comes from the 1958 Silhouettes' hit, "Get A Job."

256 A: Francis Scott Key wrote the American national anthem after watching the unsuccessful bombardment of Baltimore's Fort McHenry by British ships on the night of September 14, 1814.

257 A: In 1823, President James Monroe officially declared that the Americas were to be free from colonialism and interference from Europe.

258 A: Under siege by thousands of Mexican soldiers led by dictator Santa Ana, the 189 defenders of the Texas Republic at the Alamo held out for thirteen days to the last man. Among the illustrious, doomed defenders were William Travis, Davy Crockett, and Jim Bowie.

259 A: The first canal boat left Buffalo on October 26, 1825, and arrived in New York City on November 4. By connecting Lake Erie to the Hudson River, the canal radically decreased the shipping time between cities in the interior and the Atlantic coast.

260 A: The peregrine falcon can reach speeds of up to 200 miles per hour when diving for more sluggish prey, such as doves and pigeons.

261 Q:
Which species is the largest living bird?

262 Q:
What is the world's smallest living bird?

263 Q:
Where do secretary birds live? How do they subdue their prey?

264 Q:
Do birds have a sense of smell?

265 Q:
Do any mammals lay eggs?

266 Q:
What kind of animal is a pinniped?

261 A: The ostrich. Male ostriches grow to about eight feet tall and weigh 300 pounds. They may be flightless birds, but ostriches are fast on their feet, capable of running forty-five miles per hour.

262 A: The bee hummingbird, native to Cuba, weighs less than one ounce and measures about two inches.

263 A: Secretary birds, three-foot-tall birds with long legs, live in sub-Saharan Africa. These birds of prey use their strong legs to kickbox, pounding the daylights out of reptiles, snakes, lizards, and small rodents. They are named secretary birds because the plume feathers at the back of their heads resemble old-fashioned quill pens.

264 A: Yes, but based on bird brain studies, the sense of smell seems to be underdeveloped in most birds. Not too surprisingly, a large part of their cranial matter is devoted to sight and balance—both very important attributes when flying.

265 A: Yes, both the spiny anteater and the duck-billed platypus are mammals and lay eggs.

266 A: A pinniped is an aquatic carnivorous mammal that has four flippers. The name "pinniped" refers to the animal being "fin-footed." Seals, sea lions, and walruses are all pinnipeds.

267 Q:

What is the largest pinniped?

268 Q:

What is a polar bear's favorite treat?

269 Q:

What movie has won the most Academy Awards?

270 Q:

For what movie did Humphrey Bogart win his only Best Actor Oscar?

271 Q:

What two actors won Oscars for playing the same character in two different films?

272 Q:

Name the classic epic movie—an Academy Award winner for Best Picture—that has no female speaking roles.

273 Q:

Ingrid Bergman won her second Best Actress Oscar for this film that also marked her return to Hollywood.

274 Q:

Elizabeth Taylor won two Best Actress Academy Awards. Name the two movies.

267 A: The largest pinniped is the elephant seal, which can weigh as much as four tons.

268 A: Polar bears, the world's largest land predators, like to eat seals.

269 A: It's a three-way tie. *Titanic* (1997), *Ben Hur* (1959), and *The Lord of the Rings: The Return of the King* (2003) each won eleven Oscars.

270 A: *The African Queen* (1951).

271 A: Marlon Brando won Best Actor for playing aged Don Vito Corleone in *The Godfather* (1972). Robert DeNiro won Best Supporting Actor for his portrayal of the younger Vito Corleone in *The Godfather Part II* (1974).

272 A: *Lawrence of Arabia* (1962).

273 A: *Anastasia* (1956).

274 A: *Butterfield 8* (1960) and *Who's Afraid of Virginia Woolf?* (1966).

275 Q:
Where was the game of golf invented?

276 Q:
Who has won more Masters tournaments than any other golfer?

277 Q:
When did Tiger Woods win the Masters tournament for the first time?

278 Q:
Who was the first president to take up golf?

279 Q:
Who among the following is not a member of the Professional Bowlers Association Hall of Fame?

   a. Dave Ferraro
   b. Carmen Salvino
   c. Don Carter
   d. Roy Buckley

280 Q:
Who was the first elected president of Russia?

275 A: Scotland is considered the birthplace of the sport, golf having flourished there since the fifteenth century. Even then, accounts tell us, an exerting round was often followed by a refreshing trip to the local tavern.

276 A: Jack Nicklaus, with six Masters victories.

277 A: Woods won his first Masters jacket on April 13, 1997, thus becoming the first man of color to gain that coveted title.

278 A: William Howard Taft, who, despite some religious protests, inspired an American golf boom with his enthusiastic play.

279 A: They all are.

280 A: Boris Yeltsin, who was elected in June 1991.

281 Q:

What was the name of the dynasty that ruled Russia from 1613 to 1917?

282 Q:

Who was Russia's famous "Mad Monk"?

283 Q:

How did Rasputin die?

284 Q:

What is the highest waterfall in the world?

285 Q:

What is the highest waterfall in North America?

286 Q:

How high is Niagara Falls?

287 Q:

Where is the world's largest desert?

281 A: The Romanovs. Descended from Michael Romanov, this dynasty included Peter the Great, Catherine the Great, and two Alexanders. Czar Nicholas II, the last Romanov ruler, was forced to abdicate in 1917.

282 A: Grigori Rasputin was a Siberian peasant farmer and faith healer who wielded great influence with the imperial Russian ruling family. Alexis, the son and heir to the Russian throne, suffered from hemophilia, the bleeding disease, and Czarina Alexandra believed that Rasputin could heal him.

283 A: On the night of December 16–17, 1916, three political opponents endeavored to kill Rasputin. First, they poisoned him, but it had no effect. Then, they shot him repeatedly, but, despite a torrent of bullets, Rasputin was still standing. Then the would-be assassins threw the notorious giant into the Neva River, where eventually he drowned.

284 A: Angel Falls, on the Carrao, in Venezuela, at 3,212 feet.

285 A: Yosemite Falls, in California, with a total drop of 2,425 feet.

286 A: Canada's Horseshoe Falls is 167 feet high and 2,600 feet wide; the American Falls is 176 feet high and 1,000 feet wide.

287 A: The Sahara, in North Africa, encompasses 3,500,000 square miles.

288 Q:

What is the largest desert in North America?

289 Q:

In a 1946 film, Fred Derry, Homer Parrish, and Al Stevenson land at the airport in a town called Boon City. Why have they come?

290 Q:

In a 1954 film, an ex-soldier arrives in a town called Suddenly. What has he come to do? What is the name of the film, and who plays the main character?

291 Q:

Peter Lorre gets them and hides them in Humphrey Bogart's place of business. Bogart spends the film denying he has them, but finally gives them away. In the end, everybody's more or less happy. What are these mysterious articles and what is the film?

292 Q:

In this film, Peter Lorre goes to Humphrey Bogart's place of business in order to find something. Bogart denies having it, but finally gives it to the people who want it. In the end, everybody's more or less unhappy. What is it and in what movie does it appear?

288 A: Though tiny compared to the Sahara, the Chihuahuan gains that honor. Its 140,000 square miles includes parts of Texas, Arizona, New Mexico, and the country of Mexico.

289 A: They live there. It's the hometown of these three returning veterans in *The Best Years of Our Lives* (1946). Dana Andrews, Harold Russell, and Frederic March play the three.

290 A: To assassinate the president; *Suddenly* and Frank Sinatra.

291 A: The letters of transit in *Casablanca* (1942).

292 A: "The stuff dreams are made of " … the leaden, fake Maltese falcon in the movie of the same name.

293 Q:
What is the difference between a mammoth
and a mastodon?

294 Q:
What is the most prominent feature that the group of
mammals known as proboscideans has in common?

295 Q:
Dolphins call to each other, but do they have vocal
cords?

296 Q:
Why did the United States Navy use trained
dolphins in Vietnam?

293 A: Glad you asked. Both are prehistoric proboscideans, but mammoths lived in grasslands, were ten to fourteen feet tall, and could weigh up to 20,000 pounds. Mastodons lived in forests, were only six to ten feet tall, and weighed only 8,000 to 10,000 pounds. Mastodons had flat heads and short tusks; mammoths had rounded heads and long tusks. Frozen, preserved mammoths have been found, organs intact, in the Siberian permafrost. Both species were herbivores.

294 A: These mammals all carry a long trunk-like snout. There are only two extant proboscideans—the African (*Loxodonta africana*) and Asian (*Elephas maximus*) elephants. Elephants are also called pachyderms, a term that refers to their thick skin.

295 A: Dolphins, who are aquatic mammals, do not have vocal cords, nor do they speak with their mouths. They are able to make noises using their breath through the blowholes on the tops of their bodies.

296 A: Dolphins were trained to conduct surveillance patrols with a camera held in their mouths, and to work with frogmen to deliver equipment and locate underwater mines and obstacles. The United States Navy also used trained dolphins in 1987 in the Persian Gulf. Officials deny rumors, however, that the dolphins have been used to attack enemy ships and swimmers.

297 Q:
What is unusual about pregnant seahorses?

298 Q:
What is a marsupial?

299 Q:
Where was the first skyscraper built?

300 Q:
What is the tallest building in the world?

301 Q:
What is the tallest building in the United States?

302 Q:
What is the largest office building in the world, in terms of ground space?

297 A: Pregnant seahorses are male. The female seahorse transfers her eggs into the male's exterior abdominal pouch. The male grows visibly "pregnant" within a few weeks. Embryos hatch in his pouch and are incubated there.

298 A: These are mammals with a pouch on the abdomen of the female, such as kangaroos, bandicoots, wombats, koalas, and opossums.

299 A: The building considered to be the world's first skyscraper is William Le Baron Jenney's ten-story Home Insurance Company Building in Chicago. Built in 1883, it was the first fully steel-framed building, using steel-girder construction, and supported by internal construction, rather than by load-bearing walls.

300 A: At 2,723 feet, Dubai's Burj Khalifa towers over any other manmade structure in the world.

301 A: The Willis Tower in Chicago, which was formerly known as the Sears Tower, is 110 stories and 1,450 feet tall, and is the seventh-tallest building in the world. It was completed in 1974.

302 A: The Pentagon, which was built in sixteen months in 1941–43, covers thirty-four acres, and has a gross floor area of 6.6 million square feet, not to mention 7,748 windows.

303 Q:

Which tenor received a record 165 curtain calls?

304 Q:

The Ryman Auditorium is well known as the home of what musical event? Where is it?

305 Q:

What popular recording artist had a 1957 hit version of Little Richard's "Tutti Frutti" and then returned four decades later with a CD of heavy metal music?

306 Q:

"More stars than there are in the heavens" was a 1940s slogan of which Hollywood studio?

307 Q:

After two decades of song and dance musicals in which he usually played an actor/dancer, Fred Astaire took a dramatic role as a scientist on a submarine. Can you name the movie?

308 Q:

Her real name was Ruby Stevens, and for more than a decade, she was married to an actor whose birth name was Spangler Arlington Brugh. Under what names did they become immensely popular stars?

303 A: Tenor Luciano Pavarotti grew tired answering the audience's call at a Berlin Opera House appearance in 1988.

304 A: *The Grand Ole Opry*, which has been a radio program for seventy-five years, moved to the Ryman Auditorium in 1943, and stayed there until the new Opry House was built in Opryland in 1974. The Ryman Auditorium is on 5th Avenue North in Nashville, Tennessee.

305 A: Pat Boone followed up his Top 40 Little Richard cover with his 1997 *Metal Mood* tribute album.

306 A: MGM.

307 A: *On the Beach* (1959).

308 A: Barbara Stanwyck and Robert Taylor.

309 Q:
Where was William Shakespeare born?

310 Q:
In what year was the Globe Theater built?

311 Q:
When was Christopher Marlowe born? How did he die?

312 Q:
Which Elizabethan dramatist narrowly escaped
the gallows for murder?

313 Q:
What is the name of William Shakespeare's wife?

314 Q:
What did Shakespeare famously bequeath to his wife?

315 Q:
Who fought in the Trojan Wars?

309 A: Fittingly, the Stratford Bard was born in Stratford-upon-Avon, England. He died on April 23, 1616, exactly fifty-two years after his birth.

310 A: In 1599, the theater most associated with Shakespeare was constructed, utilizing timbers from another acting venue.

311 A: Like Shakespeare, Marlowe was born in 1564. He was killed in a tavern brawl on May 30, 1593.

312 A: Ben Jonson. In 1598, this scrappy playwright was almost executed for killing a fellow actor in a duel. Although he was reprieved, he was branded on the thumb for the felony.

313 A: Anne Hathaway. In 1582, Shakespeare married this farmer's daughter. She was twenty-six; he was eighteen.

314 A: The only item Shakespeare specifically willed to his spouse was his "second best bed." Because the best bed in Elizabethan times was traditionally reserved for visitors, Shakespeare's bequest might have been a sign of endearment, rather than the slight it first seems. In any case, by law, Anne Hathaway received one-third of her husband's estate.

315 A: A coalition of Greek principalities fought against Troy. This war was the subject of Homer's *Iliad*. It is believed that the wars took place in the twelfth century BCE.

316 Q:
What was the Trojan Horse?

317 Q:
Who were the combatants in the Persian Wars?

318 Q:
Which ancient city-states were the main adversaries in the Peloponnesian Wars?

319 Q:
Match the U.S. cities and their nicknames.

Detroit . . . . The Windy City

New York. . . . . Big D

New Orleans . . . . The Motor City

Chicago. . . . . The Big Easy

Dallas . . . . The Big Apple

316 A: According to classical literature, Odysseus conceived the clever idea of smuggling Achaean troops concealed in a wooden horse into Troy to defeat the hostile Trojans. Contrary to popular opinion, the horse was not presented to the unsuspecting Trojans as a gift: It was simply left in the abandoned Achaean camp outside the city walls. The Trojans took the bait, and the city was conquered.

317 A: The Greeks fought against the Persians for more than forty years, from 521–479 BCE. Herodotus's *History* provides much of the surviving information on this war.

318 A: Sparta and Athens. The First Peloponnesian War lasted from 431–421 BCE; the second ended in 404 BCE with Athens surrendering to Sparta. After this defeat, Athens went into a decline.

319 A:
Detroit = The Motor City
New York = The Big Apple
New Orleans = The Big Easy
Chicago = The Windy City
Dallas = Big D

320 Q:
Name the presidents portrayed on Mount Rushmore.

321 Q:
What was the first capital of the United States?

322 Q:
What does the state name "Oklahoma" mean in the Choctaw language?

323 Q:
Which city is further east—Key West, Florida, or Lima, Peru?

324 Q:
Who was the title character of the 1963–66 television series *My Favorite Martian*?

325 Q:
When was the first episode of *I Love Lucy* shown?

326 Q:
What was the name of the club Ricky Ricardo owned on *I Love Lucy*?

327 Q:
What is Lucy's maiden name?

320 A: From viewer's left to right: George Washington, Thomas Jefferson, Theodore Roosevelt, Abraham Lincoln.

321 A: Both New York City and Philadelphia have a claim to the honor. George Washington was inaugurated as the first president at New York's Federal Hall and the first sessions of Congress under the Constitution were convened in that city. However, Philadelphia was considered the de facto capital at the time of the Declaration of Independence.

322 A: The name "Oklahoma" comes from the Choctaw words: *okla* meaning "people" and *humma* meaning "red," so the state's name literally means "red people."

323 A: Lima, Peru, at longitude 77° west, is four degrees east of Key West at 81° west. In fact, most of South America is east of North America.

324 A: Ray Walston played the Martian who, disguised as Uncle Martin, lives with Timothy O'Hara (Bill Bixby).

325 A: On October 15, 1951, CBS broadcast the first *Lucy* show. The episode was entitled "The Girls Want to Go to a Nightclub." The original show's run continued through 1957.

326 A: The Ricky Ricardo Babalu Club. He originally worked at the Tropicana.

327 A: MacGillicuddy.

328 Q:

For many viewers, the family on the 1970s sitcom *The Brady Bunch* was too good to be true. What did Mike Brady do for a living to support his incredibly ideal brood?

329 Q:

The Brady boys were lucky enough to get visits from several famous athletes. Can you name the famous major league ballplayer and NFL star who made guest appearances?

330 Q:

Years before he appeared as a guest on *The Brady Bunch,* that same baseball player was on another TV sitcom. Which one?

331 Q:

Athletes have appeared as guest stars on TV shows for years. What major league manager showed up on *The Beverly Hillbillies* to scout Jethro?

332 Q:

How do frogs tell us that the air pressure is decreasing?

333 Q:

Do ducks sleep with their eyes closed?

328 A: Mike Brady, played by Robert Reed, was an architect.

329 A: Dodger pitcher Don Drysdale and NFL Hall of Famer Joe Namath both stopped by the Brady home to share tips and good will.

330 A: *Leave It to Beaver*, where Don Drysdale took a long-distance call from The Beav and Gilbert.

331 A: Leo Durocher made a guest appearance on this 1960s series.

332 A: Frogs croak more often when air pressure drops. Low air pressure brings stormy weather.

333 A: Yes and no. Ducks in the center of a group sleep with their eyes shut, but quackers on the edges will spend the night with one eye open.

334 Q:
How much gas do cows belch?

335 Q:
How far does a skunk spray?

336 Q:
When was Scrabble invented?

337 Q:
What is the best-selling board game on earth and who invented it?

338 Q:
How old is chess?

339 Q:
What two letters are not on the telephone dial?

334 A: Every day, the average cow emits thirty-five cubic feet of methane gas. (Is this why cows are seldom invited to parties?) Conferences on global warming have seriously discussed this embarrassing problem.

335 A: These little stinkers can spray their foul-smelling liquid up to ten feet. Even worse, this pungent aroma can drift downwind as far as a mile and a half.

336 A: Unemployed architect Alfred M. Butt invented the game in 1931, but he couldn't settle on a name. He called his diversion "Lexiko," "It," and "Criss Cross," but made few sales. He and his partner James Brunot didn't produce games to be sold until 1948.

337 A: Charles B. Darrow of Germantown, Pennsylvania, is generally credited with having invented the game of Monopoly in 1933.

338 A: The prehistory and early history of chess are matters of great dispute. However, Chaturanga, which developed in India in the sixth century, has a strong claim to be the earliest clear ancestor of chess. The game entered Europe around the tenth century.

339 A: "Q" and "Z."

340 Q:

What famous Egyptian city was founded by Alexander the Great in 331 BCE?

341 Q:

In what country are the remains of the ancient city of Petra?

342 Q:

Who were the Vandals?

343 Q:

Who were the original Young Turks?

344 Q:

Only three presidential candidates won at least 520 electoral votes in their race for the White House. Who are they?

345 Q:

Name the four chief executives who won the White House after being defeated as presidential candidates.

340 A: After Alexander the Great conquered Egypt, he established Alexandria, naming the port city in his own honor.

341 A: The city, which was founded by Nabataean Arabs, is located in present-day Jordan. Once an important trading center, the abandoned metropolis was forgotten by the Western world for centuries before being rediscovered in the early nineteenth century.

342 A: They were a Germanic tribe that conquered Spain and Gaul and sacked Rome in the fifth century.

343 A: The Young Turks were a coalition of Turkish nationalists and other reformers who, in 1908, seized power and forced the Sultan to restore a constitution and introduce social reforms, secularization, and industrialization in the Ottoman Empire.

344 A: Franklin Delano Roosevelt garnered 523 in 1936; Richard Nixon, 520 in 1972; and Ronald Reagan, 525 in 1984. Each of them was running for a second term.

345 A: Thomas Jefferson, Andrew Jackson, William Henry Harrison, and Richard Nixon. Sixteen years before Franklin Delano Roosevelt became president in 1936, he had been defeated as a vice presidential candidate.

346 Q:

All except one of the following presidents was defeated when he was seeking reelection. Name that president.

John Adams   Grover Cleveland
William McKinley   John Quincy Adams
Gerald Ford   William Howard Taft
George H. W. Bush   Benjamin Harrison
Martin Van Buren   Jimmy Carter
Herbert Hoover

347 Q:

What real-life couple met and fell in love as the stars of *Bridget Loves Bernie*?

348 Q:

What was the single biggest problem that Steven and Elyse Keaton (played by Michael Gross and Meredith Baxter) had with their teenage son Alex?

349 Q:

What Oscar-winning actor made a guest appearance playing Michael J. Fox's uncle on *Family Ties*?

350 Q:

In what year did *The Beverly Hillbillies* first rumble into Hollywood, California?

346 A: William McKinley was elected in both 1896 and 1900. Unfortunately for him, he was assassinated in 1901.

347 A: Meredith Baxter became Meredith Baxter Birney after she fell in love with actor David Birney while they were playing Bridget and Bernie Steinberg on this early 1970s sitcom. The marriage lasted longer than the show, but it eventually ended as well.

348 A: Alex (Michael J. Fox) was a conservative Republican. Elyse and Steven, his parents, were liberals. *Family Ties* aired from 1982 to 1989.

349 A: Tom Hanks.

350 A: *The Beverly Hillbillies*, which starred Buddy Ebsen as the nouveau riche oil tycoon Jed Clampett, was first broadcast in 1962.

351 Q:

One of the biggest questions of the early 1980s was "Who Shot J. R.?" So, who did deliver the fatal shot on *Dallas*?

352 Q:

On the long-running series *Bonanza* (1959–73) there were three Cartwright boys. Name the actors and the characters.

353 Q:

What was the name of the Cartwright's ranch on *Bonanza*?

354 Q:

Who played Commander Adama on the late-1970s sci-fi series *Battlestar Galactica*?

355 Q:

Who sewed the first American flag?

356 Q:

How many pounds of jelly beans were ordered by the White House during the Reagan administration?

357 Q:

For whom was the teddy bear named?

351 A: Inveterate schemer J. R. Ewing, played by Larry Hagman, was shot by his sister-in-law Kristin, played by Mary Crosby. Kristin was driven to a murderous rage when J. R. refused to marry her, as he had promised.

352 A: Pernell Roberts played Adam; Dan Blocker played Hoss; and Michael Landon played Little Joe.

353 A: The Ponderosa.

354 A: Lorne Greene, who also starred as the father of the Cartwright boys on *Bonanza*.

355 A: Betsy Ross. Some rude debunkers have claimed that the Ross flag story was made out of whole cloth, but most historians and vexillologists (flag experts) agree that the widowed seamstress did indeed create the first American flag.

356 A: To satisfy Ronald Reagan's well-known passion, twenty-four thousand pounds of jellybeans were ordered—and presumably consumed—by the staff of the White House during his two terms.

357 A: No other than President Theodore "Teddy" Roosevelt. While on a hunting trip in 1902, Teddy insisted that the hunting party put a wounded bear out of its misery. Eventually, with the help of cartoonist Clifford Berryman, the story changed to Teddy "rescuing" a wounded bear cub. Shortly thereafter, enterprising toy manufacturers named their toy bears "teddy bears."

358 Q:

Which president gave the shortest inauguration address?

359 Q:

Eight presidents were born in one state. Can you identify the state and the presidents?

360 Q:

What ringing comment did Harry S. Truman make concerning friendship in Washington, D.C.?

361 Q:

What is unique about Pluto's orbit around our sun?

362 Q:

What is the highest mountain in South America?

363 Q:

Which mountain is the highest point on the continent of Africa?

364 Q:

What is the highest point in Australia?

358 A: George Washington's second inaugural speech lasted only two minutes. It consisted of a mere 133 words.

359 A: Virginia. The eight presidents born within its borders were Washington, Jefferson, Madison, Monroe, William Henry Harrison, Tyler, Taylor, and Wilson. The runner-up state is Ohio, with seven presidential births: Grant, Hayes, Garfield, Benjamin Harrison, McKinley, Taft, and Harding.

360 A: As quoted by Helen Thomas, UPI White House correspondent, Truman said, "If you want a friend in Washington, get a dog."

361 A: Two things. First, Pluto's transit is not a circular orbit, but an elongated ellipse that takes 248 years to complete. For that reason, Pluto, the ninth planet, was closer to the sun for the last twenty years than the eighth planet was. Second, Pluto manifests an unusual tilt of seventeen degrees to the plane in which Earth and the other planets orbit.

362 A: Mount Aconcagua in the Argentine Andes is 22,834 feet above sea level.

363 A: Hemingway's favorite climb, Mount Kilimanjaro in Tanzania, ranks as the highest mountain in Africa at 19,340 feet.

364 A: At 7,310 feet, puny by most standards, Mt. Kosciusko is nevertheless the highest mountain on the continent Down Under.

365 Q:

Which of the fifty United States has the lowest high point?

366 Q:

On what day did Washington cross the Delaware?

367 Q:

Besides Paul Revere, who else warned the good people of Concord that the British were coming?

368 Q:

Which American military leaders captured Fort Ticonderoga?

369 Q:

How did Alexander Hamilton die?

370 Q:

Where was Frank Sinatra born?

371 Q:

What was the name of Sinatra's first group?

372 Q:

For what role did Sinatra win his Oscar?

365 A: Florida. No point in the Sunshine State is higher than Britton Hill, which is a mere 345 feet above sea level.

366 A: On Christmas Day in 1776, General George Washington crossed the Delaware River. The following day, he surprised and defeated the Hessians at Trenton, New Jersey. The Patriots' pursuit of the German mercenaries might have been slowed by their discovery of a large cache of Hessian rum.

367 A: Henry Wadsworth Longfellow's poem made Paul Revere immortal, but William Dawes and Samuel Prescott also braved that midnight ride on April 18, 1775.

368 A: Americans Ethan Allen and Benedict Arnold surprised the British and captured Fort Ticonderoga on May 10, 1775.

369 A: On July 11, 1804, Vice President Aaron Burr shot former Secretary of the Treasury Alexander Hamilton in a duel in Weehawken, New Jersey. Hamilton died the next day.

370 A: Francis Albert Sinatra was born in Hoboken, New Jersey, on December 12, 1915. He died on May 15, 1988, in Los Angeles.

371 A: The Hoboken Four. The quartet won a contest on *Major Bowes' Amateur Hour* in 1935. Frank was the lead singer.

372 A: Sinatra picked up the 1953 Best Supporting Actor award for his portrayal of Maggio in *From Here to Eternity*.

373 Q:
How many times did Frank Sinatra marry?

374 Q:
"This wallpaper is killing me" are said to have been the last words of which famous author?

375 Q:
When *Leaves of Grass* was first published in 1855, whose name appeared on the title page?

376 Q:
"April is the cruelest month" is the beginning of what major 1922 poem?

377 Q:
Early in his career, Samuel Clemens took the nom de plume "Mark Twain." What does "mark twain" mean?

378 Q:
Who is the voice of Darth Vader in the 1977 hit *Star Wars*?

379 Q:
What is the name of Han Solo's ship in *Star Wars*?

373 A: Four. He was married to Nancy Barbato from 1939 to 1951; Ava Gardner from 1951 to 1957; Mia Farrow from 1966 to 1968; and, finally, Barbara Blakely Marx from 1976 until his death in 1998.

374 A: This was reportedly the last gasp quip of the seemingly unflappable Oscar Wilde.

375 A: No one's. Walt Whitman's book might be the most important book in the history of American poetry, but its first edition was issued anonymously.

376 A: T. S. Eliot opened *The Wasteland* with those now-famous words.

377 A: "Mark twain" is a riverboat term meaning two fathoms deep (which is twelve feet). Former steamboat pilot Clemens took the name, he said, because "it has a richness about it; it was always a pleasant sound for a pilot to hear on a dark night; it meant safe water."

378 A: James Earl Jones.

379 A: The *Millennium Falcon*.

380 Q:

What kind of car is used as a time machine in the *Back to the Future* movies?

381 Q:

What was the title of the second Peter Sellers's Inspector Clouseau movie?

382 Q:

What's the name of the club featured in the 1972 Best Picture nominee *Cabaret*?

383 Q:

In *A Clockwork Orange*, Malcolm McDowell's character was particularly fond of what composer?

384 Q:

What is the name of the beleaguered country in the 1933 film *Duck Soup*? Name its president.

385 Q:

What was the last movie in which Spencer Tracy and Katharine Hepburn appeared together? And the first?

386 Q:

What movie featured the first pairing of Humphrey Bogart and Lauren Bacall?

380 A: A DeLorean.

381 A: *A Shot in the Dark* (1964). The first Clouseau movie was *The Pink Panther.*

382 A: The Kit Kat Club.

383 A: Beethoven, or as the character called him, "Old Ludwig Van."

384 A: Freedonia is led by the indomitable Rufus T. Firefly.

385 A: *Guess Who's Coming to Dinner?* (1967). *Woman of the Year* (1942).

386 A: *To Have and Have Not* (1944). It was Bacall's first film and Bogart's fiftieth.

387 Q:

Paul Newman and Joanne Woodward appeared together in which two 1958 movies? In what movie did Newman direct Woodward?

388 Q:

"Fasten your seatbelts, it's going to be a bumpy night" is one of the most famous lines in movie history. In what film was it said? What actress (and character) delivered the line?

389 Q:

When the lion roars at the beginning of an MGM movie, he's half-encircled by a Latin phrase. What is that phrase, and what does it mean?

390 Q:

What is a raptor?

391 Q:

What is unique about the migration pattern of the Arctic tern?

392 Q:

What is unique about the migration of the monarch butterfly?

387 A: *The Long Hot Summer* and *Rally 'Round the Flag, Boys!* were their first two joint projects. Newman later directed Woodward in *Rachel, Rachel* (1968).

388 A: Bette Davis (as Margo Channing) in *All About Eve* (1950).

389 A: "Ars Gratia Artis," which means "Art for Art's Sake."

390 A: Raptors are birds of prey, such as hawks and eagles.

391 A: This flighty little bird breeds in the southern sections of the Arctic, and winters along pack ice near Antarctica—11,000 miles away! The distance that it travels exceeds that of any other bird species.

392 A: The monarch butterfly migrates over 2,000 miles from its summer home in the northern United States and southern Canada to the mountains of central Mexico. The most fascinating part of this story is that the migrating butterflies have never before been to the southern winter grounds! The generation flying to the southern winter grounds was hatched the previous summer far up north.

393 Q:
What do birds dream about?

394 Q:
Is the tomato a vegetable or a fruit?

395 Q:
How did the laser get its name?

396 Q:
When did the Basque fishermen establish whaling stations in Canada?

397 Q:
Match these Canadian provinces with their capital cities.

New Brunswick . . . . **Regina**
Nova Scotia. **Victoria**
British Columbia . . . .**Halifax**
Alberta . . . . **Fredericton**
Saskatchewan . . . . **Edmonton**

398 Q:
What symbol appears on the Canadian flag?

393 A: According to a 1998 University of Chicago study, birds dream about singing. In fact, while asleep, zebra finches rehearse songs. When they awake, they warble more perfectly.

394 A: Although most people think of the tomato as a vegetable, it is actually a fruit, because it is a seed-bearing ovary of a plant.

395 A: Laser is an acronym for "light amplification by stimulated emission of radiation."

396 A: Artifacts have been found that indicate that Basque whalers were in Labrador in the sixteenth century. In fact, it is estimated that over 17,000 whales were killed and processed in Southern Labrador between 1545 and 1585.

397 A:
New Brunswick = Fredericton
Nova Scotia = Halifax
British Columbia = Victoria
Alberta = Edmonton
Saskatchewan = Regina

398 A: A red maple leaf, with eleven points. Canada adopted a new flag in 1965, doing away with the old Union Jack flag.

399 Q:
Four National Football League quarterbacks passed for more than 50,000 yards in their careers. Can you name them and their teams?

400 Q:
Which team won the infamous "Heidi Bowl"?

401 Q:
In what round of the 1979 NFL draft was Joe Montana drafted by the San Francisco 49ers?

402 Q:
Which National Hockey League team has won the most Stanley Cup championships?

403 Q:
Who holds the most scoring records in the NHL?

399 A: During his marathon 1991–2010 career, Green Bay's Brett Favre threw for an almost unbelievable 71,838 yards. Miami quarterback Dan Marino had 61,361 passing yards in his 1983–99 career. Former Indianapolis quarterback Peyton Manning, who is still active, has thrown for 54,828 yards, and John Elway, the Denver Broncos' play caller from 1983–98, passed for 51,475 total yards. Had Warren Moon not spent six years in the Canadian Football League, he would have amassed even more than his 49,117 NFL passing yards.

400 A: In November 1968, the Oakland Raiders beat the New York Jets, 43–32, by scoring two touchdowns in the last seventy-five seconds of the game. But television fans missed the last-minute heroics: In the game's closing moments, with the Jets ahead 32–29, NBC preempted the contest with the children's special *Heidi*. Needless to say, the snafu was a great occasion for outcry.

401 A: In the third round. Montana was the eighty-second pick overall.

402 A: The Montreal Canadiens, with twenty-three NHL championships.

403 A: Wayne Gretzky, who played from 1979 to 1999, finished his career holding or sharing sixty-one NHL records, including most goals scored in a season, and most goals scored in a career.

404 Q:
What is the Continental Divide and where is it?

405 Q:
Which state of the United States is the largest?

406 Q:
Which state is the smallest?

407 Q:
Match the states with their nicknames.

Pennsylvania. . . . . .Show Me State
Idaho . . . . Volunteer State
Wisconsin. . . . . .Magnolia State
Mississippi . . . . .Keystone State
Missouri . . . . .Gem State
Tennessee . . . . Badger State

408 Q:
Four states have capital cities named after American presidents. Can you name them?

409 Q:
What is the southernmost state in the United States?

404 A: The Continental Divide is the drainage divide separating rivers flowing toward opposite sides of a continent. In the United States, the Continental Divide follows the crest of the Rocky Mountains. West of the divide, the waters empty into the Pacific; east of the divide, river waters eventually flow into the Atlantic, sometimes via Hudson Bay or the Gulf of Mexico.

405 A: Alaska, which is 586,000 square miles.

406 A: Rhode Island, with 1,231 square miles.

407 A:
Pennsylvania = Keystone State
Idaho = Gem State
Wisconsin = Badger State
Mississippi = Magnolia State
Missouri = Show Me State
Tennessee = Volunteer State

408 A:
Mississippi (Jackson); **Missouri** (Jefferson City); **Nebraska** (Lincoln); and **Wisconsin** (Madison). Of course, hundreds of other American towns and cities have been named after presidents.

409 A: Hawaii, which is located as far south as 18° 55' N, at Ka Lae, on the big island of Hawaii. Key West, Florida, is the southernmost point in the forty-eight contiguous states, with a latitude of 24° 33' N.

410 Q:
Who was the inventor of the vacuum cleaner?

411 Q:
Who invented blue jeans?

412 Q:
Did Elisha Graves Otis invent the elevator?

413 Q:
Who invented the computer mouse?

414 Q:
What are the opening words of the Declaration of Independence?

415 Q:
Who wrote the Declaration of Independence?

410 A: Ives W. McGaffey devised the first vacuum cleaner in 1869. He called his crank-operated machine the Whirlwind. James Spangler of Canton, Ohio, invented the first functioning electric vacuum cleaner in 1907. It was built by the Hoover Company of New Berlin, Ohio, who rolled out their first electric Model O in 1908.

411 A: Jacob Davis, a Nevada tailor, came up with the idea of placing metal rivets on the denim at the points of strain. In 1873, he and Levi Strauss patented the process.

412 A: No, hoists already existed. But, in 1853, Otis invented the elevator brake so that elevators wouldn't fall—obviously, a necessary improvement.

413 A: Among Douglas C. Engelbart's two dozen patents is one for a "X-Y Position Indicator for a Display System," which is a prototype for the mouse. Although the device was invented in 1968, Engelbart's brainchild was not popularized until Apple used it in 1984.

414 A: "When in the Course of human Events, it becomes necessary for one People to dissolve the Political Bands which have connected them with another…"

415 A: Thomas Jefferson spent eighteen days, from June 11–28, 1776, drafting this historic document. In the process, he incorporated changes suggested by Benjamin Franklin and John Adams.

416 Q:

What is the first sentence of the Constitution of the United States of America?

417 Q:

What are the opening words of Abraham Lincoln's 1863 Gettysburg Address?

418 Q:

Who said the following: "We hold these truths to be self-evident, that all men and women are created equal"?

419 Q:

What Bill of Rights Amendment protects your right to have a trial by jury?

420 Q:

What is the Eighteenth Amendment, and when was it passed?

421 Q:

How many voting members are there in the United States House of Representatives? How many senators are there in the U.S. Congress?

416 A: "We the People of the United States, in Order to form a more perfect Union, establish Justice, insure domestic Tranquility, provide for the common defence, promote the general Welfare, and secure the Blessings of Liberty to ourselves and our Posterity, do ordain and establish this Constitution for the United States of America."

417 A: "Four score and seven years ago, our fathers brought forth upon this continent a new nation: conceived in liberty, and dedicated to the proposition that all men are created equal."

418 A: Elizabeth Cady Stanton, who made this statement at the Women's Rights Convention in 1848.

419 A: Obviously, the Founding Father believed that this was a serious issue: The Fifth, Sixth, and Seventh Amendment all address that Constitutional right.

420 A: The Eighteenth Amendment, which was adopted in January 1919, prohibited the manufacture, sale, importation, and exportation of intoxicating liquors. Prohibition was repealed by the Twenty-First Amendment, which was adopted on December 5, 1933.

421 A: There are 435 voting members of the U.S. House of Representatives; in addition, there are non-voting delegates from the District of Columbia, Guam, American Samoa, the Virgin Islands, as well as a resident commissioner from Puerto Rico. The U.S. Senate has one hundred senators.

422 Q:

How many senators does each state have in the United States Senate? How many years are there in a senator's term?

423 Q:

How many members of the U.S. House of Representatives does each state have?

424 Q:

Which states have only one representative in the United States House of Representatives?

425 Q:

Did P. T. Barnum ever serve in an elected office?

426 Q:

Was it P. T. Barnum who said, "There's a sucker born every minute"?

422 A: There are two senators from each state; each is elected for a term of six years. Mid-term vacancies are filled by appointments by state governors or legislators.

423 A: Population determines the number of representatives per state in the House of Representatives. As of 2002, the numbers of representatives per state ranges from one in states with lower populations to fifty-three representatives (California).

424 A: As of 2012, Alaska, Delaware, Montana, North Dakota, South Dakota, Vermont, and Wyoming each only have a single member of the United States House of Representatives. The District of Columbia is represented in the House by one non-voting member.

425 A: Yes. Phineas Taylor Barnum was elected to the Connecticut state legislature in 1865. He had also served as the mayor of Bridgeport, Connecticut.

426 A: Although Barnum was known for being a shameless huckster, there is no proof that he actually made that remark. In addition to his famous circus, Barnum was the showman who first presented to America the Cardiff Giant, as well as Tom Thumb, and the original Siamese twins, Chang and Eng. He began his career hawking an elderly, blind African-American woman as the supposed 161-year-old former nurse of George Washington.

427 Q:
What movie character was famous for saying, "What's up, Doc?"

428 Q:
When did Porky Pig make his first movie?

429 Q:
What are the names of the seven diminutive people in Walt Disney's *Snow White and the Seven Dwarfs*?

430 Q:
Where did Walt Disney's seven dwarfs work?

431 Q:
What is the name of the well-known Gary, Indiana, singing group that signed with Motown Records in 1969? What are the first names of the members of this group?

432 Q:
Which performer has been proclaimed the "King of Pop"? What rock-and-roller was known as the "King"?

433 Q:
Who is the "Queen of Soul"?

427 A: Bugs Bunny. Frederick Bean "Tex" Avery (1908–80) was Bugs's creator, and Mel Blanc (1908–89) provided the voice.

428 A: In March 1935, Porky Pig appeared in his first film, *I Haven't Got a Hat*, directed by Friz Freleng. Porky's Hollywood career developed alongside the career of Warner Brothers' head of animation Chuck Jones. Porky's best-known line is "Th-th-th-that's all, folks!"

429 A: In Walt Disney's 1937 adaptation of the old fairy tale, the forest-dwelling dwarfs have the names of Dopey, Sneezy, Grumpy, Happy, Bashful, Doc, and Sleepy.

430 A: These merry laborers worked in the mines, digging for diamonds. They sang "Heigh-ho" on their way to and from the mines. They also liked to whistle while they worked.

431 A: The Jackson Five. Jackie (born Sigmund), Tito (born Toriano), Jermaine, Marlon, and Michael.

432 A: Michael Jackson was dubbed the "King of Pop." Elvis Presley, who, had he lived, would have been Michael's former father-in-law, was known as the "King."

433 A: Aretha Franklin.

434 Q:
Who earned the title the "Godfather of Soul"?

435 Q:
What singer was called the "Chairman of the Board"?

436 Q:
What was the biggest hit by the soul group named the Chairmen of the Board?

437 Q:
Which father and daughter combination had a Top 40 hit singing a duet?

438 Q:
What was Elvis Presley's middle name? Where was he born? Where and when did he die?

439 Q:
Is Elvis's middle name famously misspelled?

434 A: James Brown.

435 A: Frank Sinatra, who was also known as "Old Blue Eyes."

436 A: Although the Chairmen of the Board had a few minor hits, their biggest chartbuster was their debut single, "Give Me Just a Little More Time," released in 1970 on Invictus Records.

437 A: Frank Sinatra and Nancy Sinatra had a big hit in 1967 with "Something Stupid." Two other recordings deserve honorable recognition: In 1960, Carla Thomas and her father, Rufus Thomas, recorded a song that was a hit in the Memphis area, "Cause I Love You." And in 1991, Natalie Cole sang a tribute "duet" with her late father, Nat "King" Cole, by recording her voice track with his original recording of "Unforgettable."

438 A: Elvis Aron Presley was born in Tupelo, Mississippi, on January 8, 1935. Although there are those who believe otherwise, the general opinion is that he died at the age of forty-two at his home, Graceland, in Memphis, on August 16, 1977.

439 A: Yes. Elvis's middle name is Aron, but on his grave it is rendered incorrectly as "Aaron," with two a's. People who believe Elvis is not dead point to this fact as part of the evidence of a conspiracy.

440 Q:
How many movies did Elvis Presley and Nancy Sinatra appear in together?

441 Q:
What was Elvis's profession before he became famous as a rock and roll singer?

442 Q:
What company released the first recordings of Elvis Presley?

443 Q:
Who was Colonel Tom Parker?

444 Q:
When did the United States launch its first satellite?

445 Q:
What was the name of the first human sent into space?

446 Q:
What was the name of the first American sent into space?

440 A: Just one—the easy-to-forget *Speedway* (1968), directed by Norman Taurog. Elvis plays Steve Grayson, a stock car racer who owes the Internal Revenue Service hundreds of thousands of dollars, due to chicanery by his accountant, played by Bill Bixby. Nancy Sinatra plays an IRS agent assigned to collect the money.

441 A: Elvis was a truck driver in Memphis.

442 A: Sun Records, Sam Phillips's little Memphis music company, pressed the first Elvis Presley records in 1954. "That's All Right, Mama" was on the hit side.

443 A: Colonel Tom Parker was Elvis Presley's manager. Parker had been a carnival pitchman before turning to the management of performers. He had worked with country stars Eddy Arnold and Hank Snow before becoming Elvis's manager.

444 A: The first U.S. satellite was the Explorer I, launched on January 31, 1958, almost four months after Sputnik.

445 A: Soviet cosmonaut Yuri Gagarin became the first human in space on April 12, 1961. His *Vostok I* spacecraft orbited the Earth once.

446 A: On May 5, 1961, astronaut Alan B. Shepard, Jr., became the first American in space in a fifteen-minute, twenty-eight second sub-orbital flight. John H. Glenn, Jr., became the first U.S. astronaut to orbit the Earth in 1962.

447 Q:
Who was the first woman in space?

448 Q:
Who was the first man on the moon?

449 Q:
What were Armstrong's first words when he stood on the moon's surface?

450 Q:
Where is the lunar buggy now?

451 Q:
Who was the first president of the United States to be born an American citizen?

452 Q:
For one president, English was not his mother tongue. Name the president and his first language.

447 A: Russian Valentina Tereshkova became the first woman to travel in space. She made forty-five revolutions of Earth in the spacecraft *Vostok* 6 on June 16–19, 1963. The first American woman in space was Sally Ride, who took a famous ride aboard the shuttle *Challenger* on June 18–24, 1983.

448 A: At 10:56 p.m. (EDT), July 20, 1969, American astronaut Neil Armstrong became the first person to set foot on the moon. Armstrong and Edwin "Buzz" Aldrin left the Eagle lunar landing module for more than two hours, during which time they played a little golf and rode around in the lunar buggy. Meanwhile, astronaut Michael Collins orbited the moon in the Command module.

449 A: "That's one small step for [a] man, one giant leap for mankind."

450 A: Still on the moon. Fortunately, there is no charge for parking.

451 A: Martin Van Buren was the first chief executive born in this country after the Declaration of Independence. All previous American presidents had been born as British subjects.

452 A: Martin Van Buren grew up speaking Dutch, the first language of his parents.

453 Q:

Who popularized the expression "OK"?

454 Q:

Who was the youngest person to win an acting Oscar?

455 Q:

Who is the oldest person to win an acting Oscar?

456 Q:

Only one person has won an Academy Award for playing a member of the opposite sex. Can you name him or her?

457 Q:

Name the first actor or actress to win an Academy Award for a non-English-speaking performance.

458 Q:

Who has won the Best Supporting Actor award the most times?

459 Q:

The shower scene in the 1960 classic *Psycho* is one of the most famous in film history. Name the character killed in the shower scene and the actress who played her. For bonus points, identify the city in which the movie's opening scenes occur.

453 A: There are several theories about the origin of the expression "OK"; battling proponents credit it to Native American, French, Scots, German, and even Latin. It entered the public idiom during the 1840 reelection campaign of President Martin Van Buren. Supporters shortened his nickname of "Old Kinderhook" to "OK."

454 A: At age ten, Tatum O'Neal won a Best Supporting Actress award for the 1973 film *Paper Moon*.

455 A: Jessica Tandy garnered the Best Actress award for *Driving Miss Daisy* (1989) at the ripe old age of eighty-one.

456 A: Linda Hunt won the Best Supporting Actress Oscar for *The Year of Living Dangerously* (1983). In the movie she plays a man named Billy Kwan.

457 A: Sophia Loren won Best Actress for her role in the Italian language film *Two Women* (1960).

458 A: Walter Brennan, who won three times for the films *Come and Get It* (1936), *Kentucky* (1938), and *The Westerner* (1940).

459 A: Marion Crane was played by Janet Leigh. In the movie, Marion flees her hometown of Phoenix, Arizona.

460 Q:

What inspired the colors of Krzysztof Kieślowski's film trilogy: *Blue* (1993), *White* (1994), and *Red* (1994)?

461 Q:

What director said, "I demand that a film express either the joy of making cinema or the agony of making cinema; I am not at all interested in anything in between; I am not interested in all those films that do not pulse"?

462 Q:

In which pulsing Hitchcock movie do Jimmy Stewart and Kim Novak star?

463 Q:

In the original series, what actresses played the angels of Charlie?

464 Q:

Who was the lead in the *Six Million Dollar Man* (1974–78)?

465 Q:

Maude and *The Jeffersons* both share the distinction of being spinoffs from the same show. What show?

460 A: The French flag.

461 A: François Truffaut, who directed such films as *Two English Girls* (1972) and *Day For Night* (1973).

462 A: *Vertigo* (1958).

463 A: Kate Jackson, Farrah Fawcett, and Jaclyn Smith were the original lineup. Cheryl Ladd, Shelley Hack, and Tanya Roberts were later replacements.

464 A: Lee Majors (then married to Farrah Fawcett) played Colonel Steve Austin, the test pilot who had the expensive replacement implants.

465 A: *All in the Family.*

466 Q:

What kind of car "ran great" in the theme song to *All in the Family*?

467 Q:

Another *All in the Family* question: What was Meathead's full name?

468 Q:

What business was George Jefferson in that enabled him to "move on up"?

469 Q:

Where is the Republic of Seychelles?

470 Q:

What is the largest island in the world?

471 Q:

What is the largest continent in the world?

472 Q:

We think of Europe as a continent, but is it really part of Asia?

473 Q:

How large is the United States in relation to the continent of Africa?

466 A: A LaSalle.

467 A: Michael Stivic, who was played by Rob Reiner. Meathead's run lasted from 1971 to 1979.

468 A: On the sitcom *The Jeffersons* (1975–85), George owned several dry-cleaning stores.

469 A: This little-known outpost is an archipelago consisting of 115 islands in the Indian Ocean, northeast of Madagascar. Seychelles was once part of the British Empire, but has been independent since 1976.

470 A: Greenland, in the north Atlantic, covers 840,000 square miles. The island of Australia is larger than this Danish dependency, but it is considered a continent.

471 A: Measuring more than seventeen million square miles, Asia covers nearly one-third of the earth's landmass.

472 A: According to some geographers, Europe could be considered a large peninsula of the continent of Asia, thus forming a landmass they call "Eurasia."

473 A: The U.S. would fit into Africa no fewer than three-and-a-half times.

474 Q:
Where is the Gobi desert?

475 Q:
What percentage of the world's land surface is desert?

476 Q:
Who was the shortest American president?

477 Q:
Who was the tallest American president?

478 Q:
Victor Fleming won the 1939 Academy Award for Best Director for *Gone With the Wind,* which also won Best Picture. Fleming directed another movie nominated for Best Picture that year. Name it.

479 Q:
What is the name of Ashley Wilkes's plantation in *Gone With the Wind?*

480 Q:
Who played Dorothy in the 1978 film *The Wiz?* Who played the Scarecrow?

474 A: This Central Asia desert and semidesert region stretches across the Mongolian People's Republic and the Inner Mongolia region of China, its total area comprising approximately 500,000 square miles.

475 A: Twenty.

476 A: James Madison stood only five feet four inches tall. He was probably also the lightest American president in history, weighing in at only one hundred pounds.

477 A: Easy. Abraham Lincoln was six feet four inches.

478 A: *The Wizard of Oz.*

479 A: Ashley, played by Leslie Howard, owns "Twelve Oaks."

480 A: Diana Ross played Dorothy, and Michael Jackson played the Scarecrow.

481 Q:
The A-Team was a quintessential 1980s action show. What were the character names of the four men who comprised the A-Team?

482 Q:
Who were the world's first surfers?

483 Q:
What name did Captain Cook give the islands we now call Hawaii?

484 Q:
Where did the sandwich get its name?

485 Q:
What is the latitude of the equator?

486 Q:
What is the longitude of the prime meridian?

481 A: Hannibal, Face, Murdock, and B. A. Baracus.

482 A: Certainly not Europeans. When Captain James Cook "discovered" the Hawaiian Islands in 1778, riding the ocean waves on a narrow surfboard was already a popular sport.

483 A: In 1778, English Captain Cook named his discovery the Sandwich Islands, in honor of the Earl of Sandwich.

484 A: John Montagu, the Fourth Earl of Sandwich (1718–92), was a British nobleman who served as the secretary of state and first lord of the admiralty, and is credited with popularizing sandwiches. He loved to gamble, and hated to leave the gaming table. Having meat served between two slices of bread enabled him to eat while he stayed in the game. Soon, this food creation was named after him.

485 A: The equator is a great circle around the earth that has a latitude of zero degrees. It is the baseline from which latitude is calculated over the globe. The equator is equidistant from the two geographical poles, dividing the earth into the Northern and Southern Hemispheres.

486 A: The prime meridian has a longitude of zero degrees and runs through Greenwich, England. It separates the east and west longitudes.

487 Q:
What is the International Date Line?

488 Q:
When a new London Bridge was built in 1973, its 1831 predecessor was taken down. Where is it now?

489 Q:
Where is the Ponte Vecchio?

490 Q:
Why is the bridge in Venice named the "Bridge of Sighs"?

491 Q:
What was the Tay Bridge Disaster?

487 A: The International Date Line, halfway around the earth from Greenwich, roughly following the 180° meridian, is the line where each calendar day begins. The date on the western side of the line (in the Eastern Hemisphere) is one day later than the date on the eastern side of the line (in the Western Hemisphere).

488 A: The old London Bridge is now in Lake Havasu City, Arizona. Designed by John Rennie, the Thames-crossing span was itself a replacement for the medieval London Bridge of nursery rhyme fame.

489 A: Considered to be an outstanding engineering achievement of the Italian Middle Ages, this much-photographed bridge crosses over the Arno River in Florence.

490 A: The seventeenth-century bridge over the Rio di Palazzo received its nickname because it served as a prisoner's path from his cell to the dreaded inquisitor's rooms in the main palace.

491 A: The two-mile-long railway bridge over Scotland's Firth of Tay opened in 1878, but collapsed just a year later during a severe December storm, killing all seventy-five passengers and crew aboard a crossing train. The disaster shocked the general public, inspired a famous poem, and sent shock waves through the Victorian engineering profession.

492 Q:
In 1940, the Tacoma Narrows Bridge received an unwelcome nickname. What was the nickname and what was its cause?

493 Q:
H. L. Mencken single-handedly engineered an indoor plumbing hoax. Can you flush it out?

494 Q:
Speaking of bathtubs, why did William Howard Taft's bathing place to have to be replaced?

495 Q:
During which administration were electric lights added to the White House?

496 Q:
Who made the first presidential phone call?

497 Q:
Who installed a bowling alley in the White House?

498 Q:
On June 2, 1886, a historic event occurred at the White House. What was it?

492 A: This bridge across Puget Sound became known as "Galloping Gertie," because less than five months after it opened, it twisted, buckled, and rolled under gale-force winds. Mercifully, "Gert" was replaced in 1950 by a newer, safer span.

493 A: In 1917, the famed Baltimore journalist wrote a much-quoted column that asserted that President Millard Fillmore installed the first bathtub in the White House. By the time Mencken confessed the ruse ten years later, his story had gained wide acceptance. To this day, it remains unclear who was the first U.S. president to become totally clean.

494 A: A new and larger bathtub needed to be installed after the 332-pound Taft became hopelessly stuck while taking an executive bath. It is said that it took six men to extricate the naked commander in chief.

495 A: Benjamin Harrison's. The illumination began in 1891.

496 A: Rutherford B. Hayes had a telephone installed in the White House in 1879.

497 A: The thirty-seventh president, Richard M. Nixon.

498 A: That day, for the first and only time, a U.S. president was married in the White House: Grover Cleveland wed Frances Folsom in the Blue Room.

499 Q:

Who was Patrick Henry? What is his famous quote?

500 Q:

Who were Mason and Dixon? What is the Mason-Dixon Line?

501 Q:

Who were Marbury and Madison, litigants in the well-known case before the Supreme Court?

499 A: This famed orator was an influential statesman and governor of Virginia at the time of the American Revolution. He is best known for saying, "Give me liberty or give me death!" at a convention in 1775. He was referring to taking up the cause of arming the militia.

500 A: In 1763, Charles Mason and Jeremiah Dixon were commissioned by the heirs of William Penn and Lord Baltimore to settle an old boundary dispute between Pennsylvania and Maryland. Proceeding along the parallel of latitude 39° 43' 17.6" N, their work was limited to the two states of Pennsylvania and Maryland. Later, the Mason-Dixon Line became known as the boundary between free states and slave states, and it is now regarded as the boundary between the North and the South.

501 A: William Marbury sued Secretary of State James Madison to force him to deliver his commission as a justice of the peace. Under the Judiciary Act of 1800, a number of new judgeships had been created; although Marbury had been appointed, he had not been formally commissioned (or paid). The importance of the case is that, in ruling, Supreme Court Chief Justice John Marshall established the judicial right to review the constitutionality of legislation.

502 Q:
When was gold first discovered in the Yukon?

503 Q:
What was the path of the Oregon Trail? What was its significance?

504 Q:
How long did it take Robert Fulton's steamship to make the river trip from New York City to Albany?

505 Q:
How many immigrants passed through Ellis Island?

502 A: On August 17, 1896, three men (Skookum Jim, Tagish Charlie, and American George Carmack) uncovered gold nuggets in Rabbit Creek, which they renamed Bonanza Creek. With that fortuitous find, the 1898 Klondike Gold Rush was on. More than 100,000 adventurers arrived over the next few years.

503 A: This 2,000-mile trail runs from Independence, Missouri, to the Columbia River region in Oregon. The trail generally follows the Platte River to its headwaters, crosses the mountains, and then snakes along the Snake River to the Columbia River. It was a path first used by fur traders and missionaries, but, beginning in 1842, wagon trains kicked off a massive move west on the Oregon Trail. Over the next twenty-five years, more than one-half million people walked and rode on this overland route, which became less important when the transcontinental railroad was completed in 1869.

504 A: Robert Fulton's first practical steamboat was no speedster. The 1807 ship made the 150-mile voyage in thirty-two hours.

505 A: Twenty-two million people passed through this New York Harbor point of entry. From 1892 to 1924, this gateway served as our country's principal immigration reception center.

506 Q:
How did the bazooka get its name?

507 Q:
What was the name of Bob Burns's radio show?

508 Q:
On *Cheers* (1982–93), Norm's wife is often referred to but never fully seen. What was her name?

509 Q:
Who played the Incredible Hulk in the 1978–82 series?

510 Q:
What Oscar-winning actress played Roseanne's grandmother on *Roseanne* (1988–97)?

511 Q:
What was the name of the nosy super on *One Day at a Time* (1975–84)?

512 Q:
Barney Miller worked at police precinct full of funny characters. What was the name of the precinct?

506 A: As unlikely as it sounds, the armor-piercing, hollow-tube weapon developed during WWII was named after the humorous musical instrument that radio entertainer Bob Burns had fashioned from two gas pipes and a funnel.

507 A: Bob Burns had a radio show that was popular in the 1930s and '40s, called *The Arkansas Traveler*. His show has been described as a precursor to *Hee-Haw*.

508 A: Vera.

509 A: Lou Ferrigno played the Incredible Hulk, and Bill Bixby was scientist Dr. Bruce Banner, during his calmer periods.

510 A: Shelley Winters.

511 A: Dwayne Schneider, played by Pat Harrington, Jr.

512 A: The 12th Precinct. *Barney Miller* aired from 1975 to 1982.

513 Q:
Why is thoroughbred horse racing called
"the sport of kings"?

514 Q:
What is the Triple Crown in thoroughbred horse racing?

515 Q:
What is major league baseball's Triple Crown? Who was
the last person to win it?

516 Q:
When did New York baseball stars first wear pinstripes?

517 Q:
In what cities did baseball's Braves make their home
before they moved to Atlanta?

513 A: Because British royalty was interested in thoroughbred racing. As early as 1110, England's King Henry I had imported an Arabian stallion from Spain, and horse racing became a favorite pastime of the English royalty and nobility. In the mid-1600s, Charles II was a racing enthusiast and did much to revive the popularity of the sport.

514 A: The three major U.S. races for horses three years of age are the Kentucky Derby, the Preakness Stakes, and the Belmont Stakes. The last horse to win all three races was Affirmed, who out-dueled Alydar in 1978.

515 A: This batting honor refers to players who lead the league in batting average, home runs, and runs batted in during the regular season. The last winner of the Triple Crown in baseball was Carl Yastrzemski of the Boston Red Sox in 1967.

516 A: On April 11, 1912, pinstripes first appeared on the uniforms of the Highlanders, the forerunners of the New York Yankees.

517 A: Boston and Milwaukee. Before they were the Atlanta Braves, they were the Boston Red Stockings (1876–83), the Boston Beaneaters (1883–1907), the Boston Doves (1908–12), and the Boston Braves (1913–52), after which they moved to Milwaukee, where they played from 1953 to 1965. In 1966, the Braves finally became the Atlanta Braves.

518 Q:

What immortal Hall of Famer finished his baseball career playing with the Braves in 1935?

519 Q:

When was the spitball made illegal in major league baseball?

520 Q:

When was the first World Series played?

521 Q:

What was the Black Sox Scandal of 1919?

522 Q:

When was the first telecast of a major league baseball game?

518 A: George Herman "Babe" Ruth played his last twenty-eight major league games for the Boston Braves in 1935. "The Sultan of Swat" announced his retirement in June of that year.

519 A: In 1920, major league baseball banned the spitball, but allowed all the pitchers currently throwing it at the time to continue to do so. When pitcher Burleigh Grimes retired in 1934 (with 270 wins), the spitball became legally dead.

520 A: Although there had been other post-season championships played as early as 1884, the first World Series Championship was in 1903. The Pittsburgh Pirates and the Boston Pilgrims (later the Red Sox) met in a best-of-nine-game postseason series in September 1903. Boston upset the favored Pirates, five games to three.

521 A: In the most famous scandal in baseball history, eight players from the Chicago White Sox (later scorned as the Black Sox) were accused of throwing the World Series against the Cincinnati Reds. The players involved were banned from professional baseball for life.

522 A: On August 29, 1939, a doubleheader between the Cincinnati Reds and the hometown Brooklyn Dodgers was broadcast on W2XBS, New York's RCA station.

523 Q:

For what activity is baseball player Moe Berg best known?

524 Q:

Trick question: Who played for the Brooklyn Dodgers for sixteen years (1940–56), but never got a hit?

525 Q:

How many bones are there in the human body?

526 Q:

How many bones are in a foot?

527 Q:

Where do you find the bones that have the nicknames of the hammer, anvil, and stirrup? What important role do they play in the human body?

528 Q:

What is the smallest bone in the body?

523 A: As a player, he was only a journeyman infielder/catcher with a .243 lifetime batting average over a sixteen-year career. But Moe Berg was also an effective spy for the U.S. government. While touring Japan in 1934 with a team that included Babe Ruth, he took photographs of Tokyo that helped guide American bombers during WWII.

524 A: Gladys Gooding, the stadium organist. The first of the stadium organists, Ms. Gooding also serenaded fans at Madison Square Garden for the basketball and hockey games of the New York Knicks and the New York Rangers. And no, she didn't score any baskets or goals either.

525 A: Adult humans have 206 bones. Surprisingly, babies have more bones than grown-ups. As children mature, bones fuse together.

526 A: Each foot has nineteen bones, fourteen of them in the toes alone. The same number of bones are in each hand.

527 A: Theses bones, formally known as the malleus, incus, and stapes, are three small bones located in the ear canal and called ossicles. Essential to the healing process, they vibrate in a chain reaction and conduct sound waves through the middle ear.

528 A: The stapes, a.k.a. the stirrup, which is located in the middle ear.

529 Q:

What were the two aspects of William Henry Harrison's 1841 inaugural address that made it historic, if not memorable?

530 Q:

Who was the first oath-taker to ride to his presidential inaugural in an automobile?

531 Q:

Who had the campaign slogan "Tippecanoe and Tyler too"?

532 Q:

Which former U.S. president joined the Confederacy?

533 Q:

Who famously said, "My country, right or wrong"?

529 A: First, it was the longest inaugural address in presidential history: This tedious harangue went on for one hour and forty minutes. Second, this lackluster occasion probably killed him. Although he was sixty-eight years old and noticeably frail, Harrison insisted on delivering his lengthy address without hat, gloves, or overcoat. The combination of the brisk March weather and a downpour took its toll. Harrison became ill and never recovered. He died exactly one month after his inaugural address.

530 A: Warren Harding was driven to his 1921 inaugural in a quite horseless buggy.

531 A: Ninth president William Henry Harrison, who led troops in the military victory over Shawnee Chief Tecumseh at the Battle of Tippecanoe (1811). John Tyler was his vice presidential running mate.

532 A: Virginian John Tyler had been the tenth president of the United States, but he was elected as a delegate to the Congress of the Confederacy in 1861. He died, however, before he could take his seat. This rebellious deed won him an unprecedented silence: His death, unlike those of all his predecessors, was not announced by the White House.

533 A: Stephen Decatur. Actually, in his original 1816 statement, Decatur said "our country," not "my country." The relevant quotation is "Our country! In her intercourse with foreign nations, may she always be in the right; but our country, right or wrong."

534 Q:

As a naval commander, Stephen Decatur fought heroically in the Tripolitan War, the Algerine War, and the War of 1812. How did this heroic warrior die?

535 Q:

Night Bus was the original title for what Oscar-winning film from the 1930s?

536 Q:

What famous movie centers around a 1905 Russian naval revolt?

537 Q:

What 1961 film included the last appearances of both Clark Gable and Marilyn Monroe?

538 Q:

At the end of *Annie Hall* (1977), who plays Woody Allen's date?

539 Q:

Who garnered the Oscar for Best Adapted Screenplay for *The Bridge on the River Kwai* (1957), and what's significant about this win?

534 A: Ironically, after surviving numerous bloody naval battles, Decatur died at the hands of a fellow American military leader. Early in his career, he served as a judge at the court-martial that convicted Commodore James Barron. After Decatur repeatedly resisted the commodore's attempts at reinstatement, Barron challenged him to a duel. On March 22, 1820, the two met on the field and exchanged gunfire. Both were wounded, Decatur mortally.

535 A: *It Happened One Night* (1934).

536 A: Sergei Eisenstein's *Battleship Potemkin*.

537 A: *The Misfits*, which featured a screenplay by Monroe's ex-husband, Arthur Miller.

538 A: Sigourney Weaver.

539 A: Pierre Boulle had written the original novel *The Bridge on the River Kwai* in French and was given credit for the screenplay, even though he had not worked on it at all. (In fact Boulle could not write in English.) Years later, the credit was changed to the real authors of the script—blacklisted writers Michael Wilson and Carl Foreman.

540 Q:
Name the first mother and daughter to receive Oscar nominations in the same year.

541 Q:
Did the film *Casablanca* win an Oscar?

542 Q:
In *Casablanca*, what was Rick's last name?

543 Q:
What was the Burma Road?

544 Q:
How many miles of public roads run through the U.S.?

545 Q:
When was Apple Computer founded?

546 Q:
When was U.S. Steel founded?

540 A: In 1991 Laura Dern was nominated for Best Actress for *Rambling Rose*. Her mother, Diane Ladd, was nominated for Best Supporting Actress for the same picture.

541 A: Yes, it won three. Its 1943 Academy Awards included Best Picture, plus individual Oscars for Best Director for Michael Curtiz, and Best Screenplay for Julius and Philip Epstein and Howard Koch.

542 A: Rick Blaine.

543 A: During World War II, this 700-mile road between Lashio, Burma, and Kunming, China, was used by the Allies for transporting supplies for use against Japan.

544 A: More than four million miles. That's enough to circle the globe 150 times.

545 A: On April 1, 1976, high school friends Steven Wozniak and Steven Jobs launched the Apple Computer Company. Before the startup, both had been working in Silicon Valley, California.

546 A: The United States Steel Corporation was formed in 1901. At that time, it was the largest business enterprise ever launched. In fact, it was the first billion-dollar enterprise in history.

547 Q:
What did Meyer Lansky have to say about the size of the organized crime industry in the United States?

548 Q:
What is the origin of the term "maverick"?

549 Q:
Who invented the guillotine?

550 Q:
What are the most valuable letters in Scrabble?

551 Q:
Match these capital cities with their countries.

Canada . . . . Budapest
Hungary . . . . Wellington
New Zealand . . . . Nicosia
Tanzania . . . . Ottawa
Cyprus . . . . Dar es Salaam
Pakistan . . . . Islamabad

547 A: "We're bigger than U.S. Steel."

548 A: Samuel A. Maverick (1803–70) was a Texas pioneer who did not brand his calves. Maverick's herd was allowed to wander, thus giving rise to the term, which denoted a stray, unbranded calf. Today, the word also refers to a human who refuses to go along with the crowd.

549 A: This swift instrument of death was devised by French doctor Joseph Guillotin (1738–1814), who argued for a quick, painless method of capital punishment. Dr. Guillotin worked together with a German engineer to create a prototype, with the blade at an oblique forty-five-degree angle. The first guillotining took place in April of 1792. During the French Revolution, thousands of men and women were guillotined.

550 A: The letters "Q" and "Z" are each worth ten points. "J" and "X" each win you eight points.

551 A:
Canada = Ottawa
Hungary = Budapest
New Zealand = Wellington
Tanzania = Dar es Salaam
Cyprus = Nicosia
Pakistan = Islamabad

552 Q:
Who were the Celts?

553 Q:
Who were the Druids?

554 Q:
What is a Gordian knot?

555 Q:
When did Alexander the Great live?

556 Q:
What was the name of Alexander's horse?

552 A: Also spelled Kelt, the Celts were an early Indo-European people who migrated over much of Europe from the second millennium BCE to the first century BCE. They ranged from the British Isles and northern Spain to as far east as the Black Sea. The native speakers of Ireland, Scotland, Wales, the Isle of Man, and Brittany all speak Celtic languages.

553 A: No one knows exactly, but it is believed that they filled the roles of priests, scholars, teachers, and judges in Celtic society. It is also believed that the stone circles found in Britain, the most well known being Stonehenge, are associated with the Druids. The earliest known records of the Druids come from the third century BCE.

554 A: In Greek mythology, Gordius, king of Phrygia, tied a knot so intricate that no one could undo it. Later, an oracle claimed that the first person to undo it would become the ruler of Asia. When Alexander the Great was unable to untie the Gordian knot, he cut through it with one stroke of his sword, thereby instructively solving a perplexing problem by a simple, decisive action.

555 A: The future King of Macedonia was born in 356 BCE and died in 323 BCE. During that brief span, he conquered much of the ancient world from Asia Minor to Egypt and India.

556 A: Buchephalas, a black stallion with a white mark on his forehead. When Buchephalas died, Alexander the Great decreed that his mount be given a state funeral.

557 Q:

Where and when was the Battle of Bunker Hill fought?

558 Q:

Did German combatants ever land in the U.S. during the Second World War?

559 Q:

What 1980s Brat Packer was originally on *The Facts of Life* (1979–88)?

560 Q:

On the 1990s show *Beverly Hills 90210*, the kids share a favorite hangout. What is its name?

561 Q:

On *Welcome Back Kotter* (1975–79), Mr. Kotter taught a group of troubled teens. What was this group of rowdy kids called?

562 Q:

Welcome Back Kotter took place in what part of New York?

563 Q:

What was the name of the suburban town where Dick Van Dyke and Mary Tyler Moore lived on the 1960s' *The Dick Van Dyke Show*?

557 A: No, not on Bunker Hill; the Revolutionary War fray was actually fought on Breed's Hill, Massachusetts, on June 17, 1775. The British troops under the command of General Howe were ordered to charge the elevated position held by the American Patriots. On their third attempt to take the hill, the Americans were forced to retreat. Although nominally a British victory, the battle showed the colonists that the British were not invincible, thus encouraging the Patriot cause.

558 A: Yes, enemy operatives landed U-boats on New York's Long Island and in Florida. At each location, four German agents were put ashore with instructions to destroy American factories. The agents from the Long Island landing were spotted almost immediately, and FBI agents were soon hot on the trail. All were eventually captured.

559 A: Molly Ringwald.

560 A: Their diner of choice is The Peach Pit.

561 A: The Sweathogs. Mega-star John Travolta started his career as Sweathog Vinnie Barbarino.

562 A: In the great borough of Brooklyn.

563 A: New Rochelle, New York.

564 Q:

On *The Dick Van Dyke Show,* what was Rob Petrie's occupation?

565 Q:

What was the name of Jerry's insistent uncle on *Seinfeld?*

566 Q:

Also from *Seinfeld*: George's fiancée died before the wedding took place. How did she die?

567 Q:

In the following list of acclaimed directors, pick the ones who have taken home Oscars for best director: Orson Welles, Alfred Hitchcock, Howard Hawks, Sam Peckinpah, Quentin Tarantino.

568 Q:

The Academy Award–winning 1996 movie *Sling Blade* was first made as a short film. What well-known actress appeared in the short but not in the full-length version?

569 Q:

What family has had three generations of Oscar winners?

564 A: He was the head writer on a TV variety show called *The Alan Brady Show*.

565 A: Uncle Leo.

566 A: Susan died from poisoning after licking the cheap envelopes that George bought to mail the wedding invitations.

567 A: As of 2012, none of them has won the Oscar for Best Director.

568 A: Molly Ringwald. Natalie Canerday took over the role in the full-length film.

569 A: The Hustons. Walter Huston won Best Supporting Actor honors for *Treasure of the Sierra Madre* (1948). Walter's son, John, took home Best Director and Best Screenplay awards for the same movie. John's daughter, Angelica, won Best Supporting Actress for *Prizzi's Honor* (1985).

570 Q:

Jack Lemmon won a Best Supporting Actor Oscar
for the role of Ensign Pulver in the 1955 film *Mister
Roberts.* What was his improbable shipboard title?

571 Q:

Where is the world's longest underground cave system?

572 Q:

Is it stalactites or stalagmites that protrude from the
ceiling of caves?

573 Q:

Who was Floyd Collins?

574 Q:

What is the Chinook wind?

570 A: Laundry and Morale Officer.

571 A: The underground labyrinth of Kentucky's Mammoth Cave National Park is the world's longest cave system. Mammoth Cave connects to the Flint Ridge cave system. The mapped underground passages have a combined length of more than 345 miles.

572 A: Icicle-shaped stalactites, which are formed by dripping groundwater, hang from subterranean passages. To remember which is which, one handy tip is that the letter "c" in stalactite stands for the ceiling, and the "g" in stalagmite is for the structure that sticks up from the ground. Sometimes, however, the two calcites meet and form solid pillars.

573 A: In 1925, this world-class spelunker was trapped by a falling rock in Kentucky's Sand Cave. He was wedged in, 150 feet below the surface, and ended up dying after being trapped for fifteen days. The new medium of radio brought the unfolding story of the attempted rescue to the living rooms of the whole country.

574 A: The Chinooks are the warm, dry winds that flow down from the eastern slopes of the Rocky Mountains and have been known to raise temperatures by thirty degrees Fahrenheit in only a few hours.

575 Q:
What is the strongest recorded earthquake in history?

576 Q:
What was the largest earthquake in the history of the forty-eight contiguous United States?

577 Q:
What is the world's largest active volcano?

578 Q:
What is the southernmost land on earth?

579 Q:
What is the northernmost land on earth?

580 Q:
What was the name of the Grammy-winning song Homer Simpson wrote on the episode entitled "Homer's Barbershop Quartet"?

575 A: A 1960 quake in Valdivia, Chile, registered 9.5 on the Richter scale. The main shock generated seismic sea waves that caused extensive damage as far away as Hawaii and Japan. The second strongest recorded earthquake was at Prince William Sound in Alaska in 1964. With its 9.2 reading, this remains the most severe earthquake in United States history.

576 A: A February 1812 earthquake centered in New Madrid, Missouri, shook with an estimated 7.7 intensity on the Richter scale. In pre-colonial days, the 1700 Cascadia quake in the Pacific Northwest, which caused widespread tsunamis, almost certainly would have exceeded an 8.7 reading.

577 A: Hawaii's Mauna Loa is a 13,677-foot rise with a dome that is seventy-five miles long and sixty-four miles wide. Its lava flows occupy more than 2,000 square miles. Fortunately, this volcano hasn't erupted since early 1984.

578 A: Antarctica, at the South Pole.

579 A: Gotcha. Unlike the South Pole, the North Pole is on an ice pack, not on land. The northernmost land is Cape Morris Jessup, Greenland, with a latitude of approximately 84° N.

580 A: "Baby on Board."

581 Q:

Homer Simpson has had quite an eclectic professional life. Which of the following jobs has Homer *not* tried?

   a. Manager for a country singer

   b. Boxer

   c. Singer in a barbershop quartet

   d. Sanitation commissioner

   e. Food critic

   f. Race car driver

582 Q:

Match the *Batman* (1966–68) villain with the actor who played him or her.

Egghead	Caesar Romero
The Riddler	Vincent Price
The Joker	Frank Gorshin
The Penguin	Burgess Meredith

583 Q:

Television's Alice was an aspiring singer, but had a day job as a waitress. Where did she work?

584 Q:

Rick Schroder played a cop on *NYPD Blue.* What was the name of the sitcom he starred in as a kid?

581 A: f. Race car driver.

582 A:
Egghead = Vincent Price
The Riddler = Frank Gorshin
The Joker = Caesar Romero
The Penguin = Burgess Meredith

583 A: Mel's Diner. The series *Alice* ran from 1976–85.

584 A: *Silver Spoons* (1982–87). He was called "Ricky" back then.

585 Q:
NYPD *Blue* was an instant hit and made several actors famous. Who was the famous actor who left after the first season? What was his character's name?

586 Q:
Who was the first woman to be elected governor of a state?

587 Q:
Which state was the first to give women the right to vote?

588 Q:
Who was "Ma" Ferguson?

589 Q:
Who was the first woman to run for the U.S. presidency?

590 Q:
Who became the first woman to head the government of an Islamic nation?

585 A: David Caruso played John Kelly.

586 A: Nellie Tayloe Ross of Wyoming was the nation's first woman governor. She won a special election in 1924 to complete her deceased husband's term.

587 A: Wyoming, which was still a territory, gave women the right to vote in 1869. Wyoming became a state in 1890, becoming the first state to grant full voting rights to women. It's not surprising: The state motto is "Equal Rights."

588 A: The first woman governor of Texas and second woman in the United States to be elected governor was Miriam Amanda Wallace Ferguson. She was the wife of former Governor James E. Ferguson, who had been thrown out of office. When Mr. Ferguson failed to get his name on the ballot in 1924, Miriam entered the race. Although "Ma" Ferguson was elected on the same day as Wyoming's Nellie Ross, she was inaugurated fifteen days later. Her nickname came from her initials.

589 A: In 1872, the Equal Rights Party nominated Victoria Claflin Woodhull for the presidency. This was at a time when, nationwide, women were not allowed to vote.

590 A: On December 2, 1988, Benazir Bhutto was sworn in as prime minister of Pakistan.

591 Q:

Who was the first woman to serve as Britain's prime minister?

592 Q:

What is the oldest domestic animal?

593 Q:

When were cats first domesticated?

594 Q:

How many American homes have reptiles as pets?

595 Q:

What breed of dog is the most popular in the United States?

596 Q:

Do all dogs bark?

597 Q:

What legendary German-born film director plays the chauffeur in *Sunset Boulevard* (1950)?

591 A: Margaret Thatcher assumed the position of prime minister in May 1979, but she had been the Conservative Party leader of the opposition since 1970. The firm leader nicknamed "The Iron Maiden" resigned her office in November 1990.

592 A: The dog, which has been sharing lives with humans for 12,000 to 14,000 years. In fact, domesticated canine ancestor gray wolves began appearing approximately 15,000 years ago.

593 A: In ancient Egypt, cats became human companions as long as 4,000 years ago.

594 A: According to a 2011–12 survey, 4.6 million American households had a reptile as a pet. Turtles, snakes, and frogs are the most popular reptilian pets. More than 72 million households own one or more pets of any kind; dogs and cats remain the most popular.

595 A: According to American Kennel Club registration tallies, Labrador retrievers are the most popular breed, followed by German shepherd dogs, beagles, golden retrievers, and Yorkshire terriers.

596 A: No. The Basenji from central Africa yodels, chortles, growls, and snarls, but never barks.

597 A: Erich Von Stroheim, who directed such films as *Greed* (1924) and *The Merry Widow* (1925). It must have been a stretch: Stroheim couldn't drive.

598 Q:
What is the name of Gloria Swanson's dead boyfriend in *Sunset Boulevard?*

599 Q:
What three Academy Awards did *Sunset Boulevard* win?

600 Q:
Name the film star and director of such silent classics as *The General* and *The Navigator* who also appeared in *Sunset Boulevard?*

601 Q:
Name the two actors who have won back-to-back Oscars for Best Actor.

602 Q:
Who has won back-to-back Oscars for Best Actress?

603 Q:
When was the modern game of tennis introduced to England?

598 A: Joe Gillis, played by William Holden.

599 A: Best Screenplay, Best Score, and Best Art Direction.

600 A: Buster Keaton, who played a card-playing friend of Norma Desmond.

601 A: Spencer Tracy won Best Actor for *Captains Courageous* in 1937 and repeated in 1938 for his role in *Boys Town*. Tom Hanks won Best Actor for *Philadelphia* in 1993 and struck gold again the following year with *Forrest Gump*.

602 A: Luise Rainer won Best Actress for *The Great Ziegfeld* in 1936 and again for *The Good Earth* the following year. Katharine Hepburn won Best Actress for *Guess Who's Coming to Dinner?* in 1967 and repeated in 1968 for her role in *The Lion in Winter*.

603 A: The standard belief is that Major W. C. Wingfield introduced lawn tennis at a garden party in 1873. He published the first book of rules for what he called "Sphairistiké, or Lawn Tennis" that year and took out a patent on his game in 1874. However, researchers have concluded that there were earlier versions of tennis, and that the first tennis club was established by the Englishman Harry Gem in Leamington in 1872.

604 Q:
When was modern tennis introduced to the United States?

605 Q:
When was the first tennis championship tournament held at Wimbledon?

606 Q:
How many Wimbledon singles tournaments did Martina Navratilova win?

607 Q:
Who was the first African-American to win the Wimbledon tournament?

604 A: Credit is given to Mary Outerbridge of New York for bringing a set of rackets and balls to her brother, a director of the Staten Island Cricket and Baseball Club in 1874. She had seen a tennis match in Bermuda. But research has shown that William Appleton of Nahant, Massachusetts, may have owned the first lawn tennis set in the United States.

605 A: In 1877, the Wimbledon club decided to hold a tennis championship, and standardized the rules. They decided on a rectangular court seventy-eight feet long by twenty-seven feet wide, and adopted a method of scoring; these decisions remain part of the modern rules. The first winner of the All-England Championship was Spencer Gore.

606 A: Nine. Her first Wimbledon win was in 1978; she also won in 1979, 1982–87, and again in 1990. Navratilova, the top ranked woman player from 1982–86, also won four U.S. Open titles, three Australian Open titles, and two French Open titles.

607 A: In 1957, Althea Gibson became the first African-American woman to win the tournament in Forest Hills, New York. That same year, she was named Woman Athlete of the Year by the Associated Press. Gibson was also the first African-American to play in the U.S. grass court championships at Forest Hills (1950), and at Wimbledon (1951).

608 Q:

Who was the first African-American male to win a major U.S. tennis title?

609 Q:

Who was Deacon Brodie? What part did he play in literature?

610 Q:

Who was the author of the 1963 novel *The Spy Who Came in from the Cold*?

611 Q:

What is George Eliot's real name?

612 Q:

When did Aldous Huxley publish his novel *Brave New World*? When was George Orwell's *1984* published?

613 Q:

Who created the great library in Alexandria in the fourth century BCE?

608 A: Arthur Ashe's fifty-one titles include the 1968 U.S. Open, the 1970 Australian Open, and the 1975 Wimbledon title. After suffering a heart attack and undergoing quadruple bypass surgery, Ashe retired as a player in 1980 with a professional record of 818 wins, 260 losses.

609 A: Deacon Brodie was the inspiration for Robert Louis Stevenson's *Dr. Jekyll and Mr. Hyde*. Brodie was a pillar of Edinburgh society who lived a double life: straight-laced establishment member turned arch-criminal, who terrified the developing capital city in the late eighteenth century. Nearly a century later, Stevenson told the story of the infamous Mr. Hyde.

610 A: John le Carré is the nom de plume of David Cornwell, who was born in 1931 in Dorset, England. Le Carré's third novel, *The Spy Who Came in from the Cold,* was the one that secured him a worldwide reputation.

611 A: Mary Ann Evans (1819–80), who is the author of many literary classics, including *Adam Bede, Mill on the Floss, Middlemarch*, and *Silas Marner.*

612 A: Huxley's view of the future was published in 1932; Orwell's story of a future society run by Big Brother and the Thought Police was published in 1949.

613 A: Ptolemy I, king of Egypt.

614 Q:
What is a theremin?

615 Q:
Where does the word "boycott" come from?

616 Q:
Who first discovered the moons of Jupiter?

617 Q:
How long did Britain's Queen Victoria reign?

618 Q:
Identify the author(s) of the following quotes?

"A penny saved is a penny earned."

"Any fool can criticize, condemn and complain, and most fools do."

"Early to bed, early to rise makes a man healthy, wealthy, and wise."

"Fish and visitors smell in three days."

"Never leave that till tomorrow which you can do today."

614 A: It is an electronic musical instrument invented by Professor Leon Theremin. The theremin is probably best known for its spooky sounds in many old science-fiction movies and in the Beach Boys' song "Good Vibrations." A musician plays the theremin by waving his hands around two electrodes that control the tone and loudness.

615 A: The term borrows its name from Captain Charles Cunningham Boycott, who was the agent for the Earl of Erne's estates in County Mayo, Ireland. In 1880, when Boycott refused to reduce rents, the tenants shunned him, and avoided any communication with him.

616 A: Galileo Galilei, who made the telescope famous with his astronomical observations in 1609. He was the first to provide drawings of the moons of Jupiter and to document the phases of Venus.

617 A: For nearly thirty-nine years. Victoria was queen of the United Kingdom of Great Britain and Ireland from 1837 until her death in 1901. Not for nothing is the latter half of the nineteenth century called the Victorian Age.

618 A: Benjamin Franklin.

619 Q:
In the United Sates, there once was a state of Franklin. Where was it located?

620 Q:
Each of the following familiar quotes is taken from a play by William Shakespeare. From which play is each taken?

"The lady doth protest too much, methinks."
"To be or not to be: that is the question."
"Something is rotten in the state of Denmark."
"To sleep, perchance to dream."
"I must be cruel only to be kind."
"The play's the thing/Wherein I'll catch the
  conscience of the King."

621 Q:
What famous American said, "You can fool all the people some of the time, and some of the people all the time, but you cannot fool all the people all the time"?

622 Q:
What famous American said, "Politics is not a bad profession. If you succeed there are many rewards, if you disgrace yourself you can always write a book"?

619 A: In August 1784, delegates from what is now eastern Tennessee gathered in Jonesborough to study the issue of seceding from North Carolina. By December, the separation was a done deal. They named the new state Franklin, after Founding Father Benjamin Franklin. The outlaw state's only governor was John Sevier, a war hero who had fought against the Indians. The state of Franklin disappeared forever when it was ceded to a new federal government in the late 1780s. It became known as the Southwest Territory.

620 A: All of them are from *Hamlet*.

621 A: The sixteenth president of the United States, Abraham Lincoln.

622 A: Ronald Reagan, our fortieth president.

623 Q:

What did President Harry S. Truman say about getting things done?

624 Q:

What is Gracie Allen's mother's solution for preparing dinner for eight people?

625 Q:

What do we call the days in which the sun's path is farthest from the equator?

626 Q:

How many medals did Jim Thorpe win at the 1912 Olympics?

627 Q:

In what year did Pocahontas marry Captain John Smith?

623 A: "It is amazing what you can accomplish if you do not care who gets the credit."

624 A: According to George Burns's wacky wife, "When my mother had to get dinner for eight, she'd just make enough for sixteen, and only serve half."

625 A: The summer and winter solstices, which fall on June 21 or 22 and December 21 or 22, are the moments in the year when the sun's path is farthest north or south from the equator. In the Northern Hemisphere, the summer solstice is the longest day of the year, measured by the amount of daylight, and the winter solstice is the shortest.

626 A: Two. In 1912, the Native American won the decathlon and the pentathlon by wide margins at the Stockholm Olympics, but the Amateur Athletic Union stripped him of his gold medals after they discovered that he had been paid to play semiprofessional baseball three years before. Decades after his 1953 death, Thorpe's amateur status was restored, and his Olympic gold medals were given to his family in 1983.

627 A: She never did. This Native American woman, whose real name was Matoaka, converted to Christianity and was baptized as Rebecca. In 1614, she married Englishman John Rolfe. Two years later, she and her husband sailed to England, where she was presented at the court of James I. Before she could return to America, she contracted smallpox and died.

628 Q:
What is the well-known story about Pocahontas that is taught to almost every American student?

629 Q:
Frank Capra, George Stevens, and William Wyler formed an independent production company that folded after making only one picture. Name the company and the movie.

630 Q:
What is the name of the doomed boat on *Gilligan's Island* (1964–67)?

631 Q:
Who invented the assembly line?

632 Q:
Who invented the radio?

628 A: Pocahontas is immortalized in American history because of the often-told story about her plea to save the life of Jamestown's military leader, Captain John Smith. In December 1607, Smith had been taken prisoner and was about to be clubbed to death by the local Native Americans, led by Pocahontas's father. Smith's rousing story eventually became embellished into the tale of Pocahontas bravely flinging herself across his body just before the club came down, declaring that he must be spared, and that she would rather be killed first.

629 A: Liberty Pictures dissolved after making *It's a Wonderful Life* (1946).

630 A: The SS *Minnow*.

631 A: Automobile manufacturer Ransom E. Olds introduced the moving assembly line in 1901. Henry Ford, who is often credited with the invention, improved it by installing conveyer belts, which speeded up the process considerably.

632 A: Guglielmo Marconi (1874–1937) was an Italian physicist and inventor of a successful system of radiotelegraphy (1895). He later worked on the development of short-wave wireless communication, which constitutes the basis of nearly all modern long-distance radio. Marconi shared the Nobel Prize in physics in 1909.

633 Q:
Who invented vulcanized rubber?

634 Q:
Who invented the zeppelin?

635 Q:
Who invented the windshield wiper?

636 Q:
Who invented modern American toothpaste?

633 A: Charles Goodyear claimed to have made the discovery that, by mixing crude rubber with sulfur and heating the mixture, the product transforms into the elastic material we know today. Unfortunately, the process that Goodyear patented in 1844 had been discovered in England by scientist Thomas Hancock, who had registered it there eight months before. To this day, the debate continues.

634 A: Count Ferdinand Graf von Zeppelin (1838–1917) was the German military officer who developed the rigid, lighter-than-air dirigible that became known as the zeppelin. The airship's first trial was in July 1900. Although zeppelins had some popularity, and passengers made thousands of trips without accidents or loss of life, these aerial vehicles are best remembered because of the tragic explosion of the Hindenburg on May 6, 1937, in Lakehurst, New Jersey. Thirty-six people died.

635 A: In 1903, Mary Anderson received a patent for this indispensable invention. Her version cleaned precipitation and debris from the car windshield by use of a handle inside the vehicle. By 1916, windshield wipers were standard issue in American cars.

636 A: English immigrant William Colgate set up a starch, soap, and candle business in 1806 in New York City. It wasn't until 1873, over twenty years after the death of the company's founder, that Colgate & Company marketed its first toothpaste, which was sold in jars. In 1896, Colgate put its toothpaste in collapsible tubes.

637 Q:

Who was the first scientist to discover the many uses of peanuts, including peanut butter?

638 Q:

Who invented the safety pin?

639 Q:

Who invented the motorcycle?

640 Q:

What French aristocrat helped the American colonists during the American Revolution?

637 A: Born a slave in Mississippi, George Washington Carver (1864–1943) developed several hundred uses for peanuts, sweet potatoes, and soybeans, as well as a new type of cotton known as Carver's hybrid. Carver dedicated his life to bettering the position of African-Americans and improving the economic prospects of the South.

638 A: This handy little device was concocted by Walter Hunt of New York, who made the discovery while he was absentmindedly twisting a piece of wire. On April 10, 1849, Hunt patented the safety pin, but he later sold the patent for a few hundred dollars. His invention has made countless babies very grateful.

639 A: By 1867, Sylvester Howard Roper of Roxbury, Massachusetts, had built a steam-powered motorcycle. But German inventor Gottlieb Daimler is credited with building the first modern motorcycle, an 1885 vehicle that was powered by a single-cylinder gas-powered engine. Daimler later teamed up with Karl Benz, forming auto producer Daimler-Benz Corporation.

640 A: Marquis de Lafayette (1757–1834) was a French aristocrat who offered his services and fought with the American colonists against the British in the American Revolution. Given a commission as a major general, Lafayette fought with distinction, particularly at the 1777 battle at Brandywine, Pennsylvania. After the war, he returned to France; on his two subsequent extended visits to the new United States of America, he was treated like a hero.

641 Q:

What French pirate helped out the Americans during the War of 1812?

642 Q:

Who played this French pirate in the 1958 film *The Buccaneer*?

643 Q:

Which scientist was the first to suggest that the Earth traveled around the Sun, rather than the other way around?

644 Q:

Who invented basketball?

645 Q:

When and where was volleyball invented?

641 A: Privateer and smuggler Jean Lafitte interrupted his pirating activities to join the fight for the United States against the British at the Battle of New Orleans (December 1814–January 1815). For his help, Andrew Jackson personally commended Laffite, and President James Madison issued a pardon for Lafitte and his men.

642 A: Dark-haired Yul Brynner was Jean Lafitte in the 1958 remake of a 1938 film. Frederic March played Lafitte in the 1938 version.

643 A: Nicolaus Copernicus (1473–1543) was a Polish astronomer who proposed that the Earth is a planet that orbits the Sun annually. This representation of the heavens is called the heliocentric, or "sun-centered," view of the planets.

644 A: James Naismith. In 1891, this strong-willed physical education teacher answered a call to create an indoor athletic activity for the students at the School for Christian Workers in Springfield, Massachusetts.

645 A: YMCA instructor William Morgan created the game of volleyball, which he called mintonette, in 1895. The breakthrough came in Massachusetts, in Holyoke, not far from Naismith's Springfield.

646 Q:
Rank these international cities by amount of average annual rainfall: San Francisco, New York, London, Dublin.

647 Q:
In what year was the "Great Blackout," when the whole Northeast of the United States lost its electricity?

648 Q:
Why are London police officers called "bobbies"?

649 Q:
When did the legendary bad boy Dick Turpin really live?

650 Q:
Who was Engelbert Humperdinck?

646 A: New York receives, by far, the most rain. Average annual precipitation, ranked by wettest to driest: New York—46.7 inches, London—29.7 inches, Dublin—29.2 inches, San Francisco—20.4 inches.

647 A: 1965. In November of that year, the northeastern United States, from Michigan to New England, as well as parts of Canada, New Jersey, and Pennsylvania, was blacked out for up to thirteen hours, due a mammoth failure of the power grid. The power outage—known as the "Great Blackout of 1965"—affected thirty million people. In New York City, people were caught in elevators and subway trains for hours.

648 A: When Sir Robert Peel introduced his Act for Policing the Metropolis in 1829, the members of the Metropolitan Police (London's first police force) were nicknamed Bobbies after Sir Robert.

649 A: Dick Turpin was born in rural Essex, England, in 1706. Captivating folklore has transformed him into a swashbuckling, devil-may-care character, but the real Turpin may have been less than that. In any case, he didn't live to enjoy his fame: He was hanged as a highwayman in 1739.

650 A: Humperdinck (1854–1921) was a German composer, whose best-known opera is *Hansel and Gretel*. Engelbert Humperdinck is also the name that Arnold Dorsey adopted in his pop music career, singing such songs as "Release Me."

651 Q:

Who was the youngest man to become president?

652 Q:

Who was the youngest man to be elected president?

653 Q:

Who was the oldest sitting president?

654 Q:

What were the station call letters where Mary Tyler Moore worked on *The Mary Tyler Moore Show*?

655 Q:

In the last episode of *The Mary Tyler Moore Show,* all the characters, save one, are fired from the station. Which character manages to keep his or her job?

656 Q:

Who was the first African-American to have his own television show?

657 Q:

What newspaper gossip columnist ended up hosting one of the most popular musical variety television shows of all time?

651 A: Theodore Roosevelt was forty-two when he stepped into the presidency in 1901 after William McKinley's assassination.

652 A: John F. Kennedy was only forty-three when he was elected president in 1960.

653 A: When he left office in 1989, Ronald Reagan was seventy-seven years old.

654 A: WJM.

655 A: The bumbling anchorman, Ted Baxter, somehow escapes expulsion.

656 A: Nat "King" Cole. His television show made history when it debuted on NBC in 1956. When the controversial breakthrough show was canceled just a year later, Cole quipped, "Madison Avenue is afraid of the dark."

657 A: Ed Sullivan. The popular *New York Daily News* Broadway columnist hosted a musical variety show every Sunday night for more than two decades (1948–71). Sullivan had his own unique diction and hand gestures, supplying comics with loads of material.

658 Q:
What television show made Dick Clark
nationally famous?

659 Q:
During the swinging sixties, two network prime-time
shows featuring pop music appeared on TV. What were
the names of those shows?

660 Q:
When was the first commercial color television
broadcast?

661 Q:
Who was the host of the *Today* show when it debuted
in 1952?

662 Q:
Which future Academy Award–winning actress was a
"Today Girl" in 1953?

663 Q:
When did Coca-Cola introduce "New Coke"?

664 Q:
What was the name of the Ramones' first album? What
were the first names of the members of the band?

658 A: *American Bandstand*. Clark hosted this popular Philadelphia-based rock and roll show, which had its ABC debut on August 5, 1957.

659 A: *Shindig* (1964–66) and *Hullabaloo* (1965–66).

660 A: On June 25, 1951, CBS broadcast a one-hour special from New York to four American cities.

661 A: Dave Garroway, who presided over the show until 1961. John Chancellor followed him with a brief stint, and Hugh Downs began his nine-year run in 1962.

662 A: Years before Estelle Parsons won the 1967 Academy Award for Best Supporting Actress for her performance in *Bonnie and Clyde*, she was on the *Today* show.

663 A: In 1985, Coca-Cola decided to change the ninety-nine-year-old formula of Coke, and introduced "New Coke." After the public outcry, they brought back a version of the original formula.

664 A: Their 1976 debut album was, surprisingly enough, called *The Ramones*. They were not related, but when they named the band, they also renamed themselves, assuming the Ramone surname. At the time of the first album, the Ramones were Joey, Johnny, Dee Dee, and Tommy. Many rock historians regard the Queens, New York-based group as the world's first punk band.

665 Q:
Why should you be concerned if your elderly grandparent suddenly likes rock and roll?

666 Q:
Does your body temperature stay constant throughout the day?

667 Q:
Why is Edith Head famous?

668 Q:
When did Americans start drinking tea?

669 Q:
When was the submarine first used in combat?

665 A: According to a recent report by researchers at Italy's National Center for Research and Care of Alzheimer's disease, sudden changes in musical taste may be an indication that an elderly person is suffering from dementia.

666 A: No. Typically, a person's body temperature rises during the late afternoon and drops late at night.

667 A: The woman born Edith Claire Posener was a dress designer who became the premier costume designer in Hollywood. During her long career, she was nominated for thirty-four Academy Awards and won an unprecedented eight Oscars. Her award-winning films are *The Heiress*, *Samson and Delilah* (both 1949); *All About Eve* (1950); *A Place in the Sun* (1951); *Roman Holiday* (1953); *Sabrina* (1954); *The Facts of Life* (1960); and *The Sting* (1973).

668 A: Governor Peter Stuyvesant brought tea to the Dutch settlement of New Amsterdam around 1650. Settlers there quickly adopted the new beverage. In fact, when the English arrived, they found that the small settlement, which they renamed New York, consumed more tea at that time than all of England.

669 A: In 1776, American David Bushnell built a human-powered, one-man submarine named the Turtle. It was able to dive and surface, and he made three unsuccessful attempts to sink British warships and break the British blockade of New York harbor.

670 Q:
When was the coronation of Great Britain's Queen Elizabeth II?

671 Q:
How many of the twenty highest peaks in the world are in North America?

672 Q:
How many of the United States' twenty highest mountains are in the forty-eight contiguous states?

673 Q:
What was the first U.S. national park?

674 Q:
Which national park has the most visitors?

675 Q:
What elements are the main components of air on earth?

676 Q:
How much of the earth's surface is covered with ice?

677 Q:
When did the so-called "Era of Good Feelings" begin?

670 A: Elizabeth the Second, Queen of the United Kingdom of Great Britain and Northern Ireland and Her other Realms and Territories, Head of the Commonwealth, Defender of the Faith, was crowned on June 2, 1953, at London's Westminster Abbey. However, she had already ascended to the British throne several months previously, on February 6, 1952, after the death of her father, King George VI.

671 A: None. All of the twenty highest peaks in the world are in the Himalayas, in Asia.

672 A: Only one. Mount Whitney, in California, is the seventeenth highest peak in the United States, at 14,494 feet. The other nineteen highest peaks are in Alaska.

673 A: Yosemite National Park, which opened on March 1, 1872.

674 A: With approximately nine million visitors a year, the Great Smoky Mountains National Park, on the Tennessee-North Carolina border, draws nearly twice the number of visitors as the second most-visited park, the Grand Canyon.

675 A: Air is primarily composed of nitrogen and oxygen.

676 A: About 10 percent of the planet's surface is covered with ice. During the last Ice Age, that proportion rose to around 30 percent.

677 A: In 1816, with the election of James Monroe.

678 Q:

Who was the author of the pamphlet *Common Sense*?

679 Q:

Who attended the Boston Tea Party on December 16, 1763?

680 Q:

"These are the times that try men's souls."
What American patriot authored this sentence?

681 Q:

Who was John Hancock? On what famous American document did he put his "John Hancock" signature?

682 Q:

What is the name of the first American patriot to die in what was called "the Boston Massacre" on March 5, 1770?

683 Q:

Which forces were victorious at the Battle of Saratoga?

684 Q:

Which forces were victorious at the Battle of Yorktown?

678 A: Thomas Paine formulated his ideas on American independence from England in *Common Sense*, published in January 1776.

679 A: Angered by the fact that the tariff on tea had been eliminated in England but not in the colonies, locals dressed in Indian disguise protested by dumping the tea from three ships into Boston Harbor.

680 A: Thomas Paine, in his pamphlet *The American Crisis*. Paine wrote sixteen influential papers, published between 1776 and 1783.

681 A: John Hancock was a prominent Boston merchant; he was the president of the Continental Congress and the first signer of the Declaration of Independence.

682 A: The first colonist to die in what was the beginning of the American Revolution was Crispus Attucks, a free black man.

683 A: Considered the major turning point of the American Revolution, the Battle of Saratoga showed the world that the American army was capable of defeating the British. After this victory, European powers, particularly the French, began to support the American cause.

684 A: The American colonial forces. Indeed, the battle at Yorktown is considered to be the final battle of the American Revolution.

685 Q:

Who were the authors of *The Federalist Papers*?

686 Q:

How long did the United States live under the Articles of Confederation?

687 Q:

What name is given to the first ten amendments to the Constitution?

688 Q:

Who was the first "real" president of the United States?

689 Q:

Where was George Washington born and when did he die?

690 Q:

To what political party did Washington belong?

691 Q:

Who was the first African-American to hold the office of secretary of state?

692 Q:

Which person gave the "Ain't I a Woman?" speech at the 1851 Women's Rights Convention in Akron, Ohio?

685 A: *The Federalist* is a series of eighty-five essays written by Alexander Hamilton, John Jay, and James Madison between October 1787 and May 1788. The essays were published anonymously, under the blanket pen name "Publius."

686 A: For eight years; from March 1, 1781, until March 4, 1789, when the Constitution was declared to be in effect.

687 A: The Bill of Rights. These amendments guarantee such basic American rights as freedom of speech, religion, and assembly.

688 A: In 1781, under the Articles of Confederation, Congress elected John Hanson of Maryland as the first president. The first president under the new system of government established by the Constitution, was, of course, George Washington.

689 A: "The Father of our Country" was born into a Virginia planter family and served his country well until he died of a throat infection in December 1799.

690 A: None. Washington was chosen to be president before the development of political parties.

691 A: Colin Powell, who was sworn in as the secretary of state on January 20, 2001.

692 A: Sojourner Truth (1797–1883). This heroic freed slave dedicated her life to preaching about the abolition of slavery and the cause of women's rights.

693 Q:

Who was the most famous "conductor" of the Underground Railroad?

694 Q:

Although making up only 1 percent of the population of the North, African-Americans made up what percentage of the Union Army at the end of the Civil War?

695 Q:

Who were the "Buffalo Soldiers"?

696 Q:

Who fought at the Battle of Wounded Knee on December 29, 1890?

697 Q:

When was the first Model T built?

693 A: Harriet Tubman, who escaped from slavery in 1849, made nineteen trips back to the South to help deliver hundreds of slaves to freedom. To accomplish her dangerous goal, she had to elude bounty hunters greedy for the $40,000 award for her capture.

694 A: By the end of the Civil War, 10 percent of the Union army were black soldiers. Many of them were freed slaves from the border states.

695 A: After the Civil War, the U.S. Congress created fighting units of African-American soldiers. They played an important role in the history of the American West. In addition to combat duties, the buffalo soldiers explored and mapped much of the Southwest, strung telegraph lines, built frontier outposts, and protected settlers from attacks. The Cheyenne named them the "buffalo soldiers."

696 A: This South Dakota battle was the last significant conflict fought between Native Americans and U.S. troops. Over 200 Sioux, led by chief Big Foot, were massacred at Wounded Knee Creek by the United States Seventh Cavalry.

697 A: Henry Ford first marketed the Model T in October 1908. Nicknamed the "Tin Lizzie," the car dominated American car sales for eighteen years.

698 Q:
What was the Manhattan Project?

699 Q:
What future American president was the Supreme Allied Commander in World War II?

700 Q:
One American general made the famous vow "I shall return" in 1942. Who was he and where was he promising to return?

701 Q:
Which future president was the skipper of the PT-109 during the Second World War?

702 Q:
Which future president was the youngest U.S. Navy fighter pilot in WWII?

703 Q:
What are the six states that were named for English kings and queens?

698 A: This immense U.S. government project involved the research and the development of the atomic bomb. With the belief that Germany might successfully develop an atomic bomb, a group of physicists, including Albert Einstein, approached President Roosevelt about establishing an atomic bomb research program. The Manhattan Project was the result.

699 A: Dwight D. Eisenhower.

700 A: The Philippine Islands. When General Douglas MacArthur was forced off the islands by the Japanese in 1942, he made his famous declaration. Two years later, he did return to drive them off.

701 A: John F. Kennedy, a junior officer and hero in the Navy. When asked about his heroism, Kennedy said, "It was involuntary. They sank my boat."

702 A: After becoming, at nineteen, the youngest Navy fighter pilot, George H. W. Bush flew fifty-eight WWII missions.

703 A: Georgia (named for George II); Maryland (for Henrietta Maria, wife of Charles I); North and South Carolina (from *Carolus*, Latin for the name Charles); and Virginia and West Virginia (for Elizabeth I, the Virgin Queen).

704 Q:

What archaeological site is believed to be the oldest known city in the Americas?

705 Q:

Who were the Aztecs? Where did they live?

706 Q:

Who were the Maya? Where did they live?

707 Q:

Where did the Incas live?

704 A: Researchers investigating an archaeological site known as Caral, 120 miles north of Lima, Peru, in the Supe River Valley, found conclusive evidence that it dates back to before 2,700 BCE, thus making it 1,500 years older than previous scientific estimations for urban civilization in the New World.

705 A: These Native Americans lived in central Mexico at the time of the Spanish conquest. The arrival of the conquistador Cortés in 1519 heralded the collapse of their great empire, which later came to be appreciated for its advanced architecture, mathematics, and art.

706 A: This major Mesoamerican civilization inhabited Central America, in what is now the Yucatan peninsula, Guatemala, El Salvador, and Honduras. The Maya, who were pyramid-builders, thrived from the fourth through ninth centuries.

707 A: The Inca civilization was centered at Cuzco, Peru. At the time of Spanish conquest in 1532, the Incas dominated the Andean area, with an empire inhabited by sixteen million people and extending some 3,000 miles, including parts of Ecuador, Chile, Bolivia, and Argentina.

708 Q:

When did the Vikings colonize Greenland and explore North America?

709 Q:

When was the first English colony founded in Newfoundland?

710 Q:

Where can you find the Blow Me Down Mountains?

711 Q:

Do any mammals fly?

712 Q:

The raccoon, a nocturnal mammal, is known for its distinctive black facial mask and alternating black and brown bands on its furry tail. What do raccoons like to eat?

708 A: Eric the Red established the first European settlement on Greenland in about 985 CE, after he had been exiled from Iceland. Eric the Red's son, Leif Eriksson, is believed to have landed in Newfoundland sometime around 1000 CE, thus making him among the first Europeans to set foot on North American soil. In 1963, archaeologists found ruins of a Viking-type settlement at L'Anse aux Meadows, in northern Newfoundland.

709 A: Sailing for England, Italian explorer John Cabot landed on the island of Newfoundland in 1497, and Sir Humphrey Gilbert claimed the settlement for Britain in 1583. Lured by the great fishing on the Grand Banks, John Guy, an English merchant, brought thirty-nine settlers to Conception Bay in 1610.

710 A: In the Blow Me Down Provincial Park in western Newfoundland, situated on a peninsula between Lark and York Harbors. These mountains also go more formally by the name of the Blomidon Mountains.

711 A: Yes, bats fly. Other mammals are superlative leapers and gliders, but only bats can actually fly.

712 A: Although they enjoy busting into campsites, breaking into houses, knocking over garbage cans, and devouring everything in sight, their supposed favorite food is small fish. Raccoons are omnivores whose diet may include grapes, nuts, insects, mice, small mammals, larvae, eggs, fish, frogs, and acorns—in other words, they eat almost anything.

713 Q:
Which president of the United States had a pet raccoon?

714 Q:
When were the first presidential candidate debates?

715 Q:
How many presidents were Roman Catholic?

716 Q:
On July 4, 1826, the United States had its fiftieth birthday. What else made that day memorable?

717 Q:
What are the two main types of clouds?

713 A: Thirtieth president Calvin Coolidge kept a pet raccoon, which he named Rebecca. This unlikely guest had been sent by some Mississippians for eating, but "Silent Cal" decided to keep it as a furry companion. Rebecca wasn't alone: Coolidge also made White House pets of a bear, a donkey, a bobcat, a lion, and a hippo.

714 A: In September and October of 1960, the nation stayed glued to the tube as Senator John F. Kennedy and Vice President Richard Nixon exchanged views in four nationally televised debates.

715 A: One. John F. Kennedy, the thirty-fifth president, who was elected in 1960.

716 A: Former presidents John Adams and Thomas Jefferson both died that day. Five years later—also on Independence Day—James Monroe died.

717 A: Cumulus and stratus. Cumulus "heaped" clouds, which are rounded on top and may be very tall, are the result of convection in unstable air. Stratus "layered" clouds are generally flat and horizontally layered. Clouds are also named according to their elevation and whether precipitation is falling. Stratus clouds at high levels, more than 20,000 feet above the earth, are called cirrus clouds; nimbus clouds are generally dark, with falling precipitation.

718 Q:
Who made the discovery that clouds could be seeded, causing it to rain?

719 Q:
What was the title of Stevie Wonder's first hit, released by Motown when he was only twelve years old?

720 Q:
In what year did the Beatles lead the British Invasion of America?

721 Q:
Where did the Rolling Stones get their name?

722 Q:
What show starred David Janssen as Dr. Richard Kimble?

723 Q:
What private eye show starred David Janssen? Who played his secretary Sam?

718 A: Dr. Vincent J. Schaefer, the father of modern weather modification, conducted the first field experiments in 1946 at the General Electric laboratory in Schenectady, New York, altering the physical processes that lead to the formation and coagulation of water droplets and ice crystals in clouds. Schaefer discovered that clouds could be seeded with dry ice or salt crystals in order to encourage the condensation of water droplets needed for rain or snow.

719 A: "Fingertips, Part 2," which hit the number-one spot in August 1963. In those days, this talented blind singer was known as Little Stevie Wonder.

720 A: The Beatles first appeared on *The Ed Sullivan Show* on February 9, 1964. Devoted fans will still remember that they performed "All My Loving," "'Til There Was You," "She Loves You," "I Saw Her Standing There," and "I Want to Hold Your Hand." Over seventy million Americans watched the show.

721 A: They took their name from a Muddy Waters tune called the "Rolling Stone Blues."

722 A: *The Fugitive* (1963–67) was the series about a doctor who has been wrongly convicted of murdering his wife, and is now on the run, searching for the one-armed man he saw running from his house the night of the murder.

723 A: *Richard Diamond, Private Detective* (1957–60). Mary Tyler Moore played Sam, but her face is never shown.

724 Q:

When did Muhammad Ali first capture the world heavy-weight crown?

725 Q:

Who won the "fight of the century" at Madison Square Garden on March 8, 1971?

726 Q:

In which different weight classes did Ray Leonard win world championships during his illustrious boxing career?

727 Q:

Name the actors who played the "Bad" and the "Ugly" in the 1966 film *The Good, the Bad and the Ugly.*

728 Q:

Name the first African-American to win an Academy Award.

729 Q:

How many years passed before another African-American won an acting Oscar? Name the actor or actress and the movie.

724 A: Ali, who was then known as Cassius Clay, defeated Sonny Liston in seven rounds on February 25, 1964, in Miami Beach, Florida.

725 A: Muhammad Ali lost his heavyweight title to Joe Frazier in a unanimous decision after being knocked down in the fifteenth round. Ali regained his title by defeating Frazier in a rematch in 1974.

726 A: In addition to winning the gold medal at the 1976 Olympics, Leonard held championships in five different weight classes: welterweight (1979), junior middleweight (1981), middleweight (1987), super middleweight (1988), and light heavyweight (1988).

727 A: The "Bad" was played by Lee Van Cleef and the "Ugly" by Eli Wallach. The "Good" was, needless to say, played by Clint Eastwood.

728 A: Hattie McDaniel won Best Supporting Actress for *Gone With the Wind* (1939).

729 A: Twenty-four years. Sidney Poitier won Best Actor for *Lilies of the Field* (1963).

730 Q:
Besides Sidney Poitier, name the other African-Americans to win Best Actor or Actress.

731 Q:
Several African-American actors besides Hattie McDaniel have won Oscars for supporting roles. Can you name them and the movies for which they won?

732 Q:
What does the Latin phrase "quid pro quo" mean?

733 Q:
How distant is the Andromeda Galaxy?

734 Q:
What celestial body is known as the "Dog Star"?

735 Q:
What is the name of the closest star?

730 A: In 2002, Halle Berry won Best Actress for her role in *Monster's Ball*, and Denzel Washington won Best Actor for his role in *Training Day*.

731 A: Louis Gossett Jr. for *An Officer and a Gentleman* (1982), Denzel Washington for *Glory* (1989), Whoopi Goldberg for *Ghost* (1990), and Cuba Gooding Jr. for *Jerry Maguire* (1996). The more recent winners are Morgan Freeman for *Million Dollar Baby* (2004) Jennifer Hudson for *Dreamgirls* (2006), Mo'Nique for *Precious* (2009), and Octavia Spencer for *The Help* (2011).

732 A: "Something for something." Quid pro quo is an exchange—something given or received in return for something else.

733 A: This immense spiral galaxy is 2.2 million light-years away from Earth.

734 A: The "Dog Star" is the brightest star in the night sky, known more scientifically as Sirius, or Alpha Canis Majoris. It is twenty times more luminous than Earth's sun, and is 8.6 light years from Earth. Some ancient cultures worshipped Sirius, including the ancient Egyptians, who constructed their temples so that light from the star could penetrate to their inner altars.

735 A: Excluding our sun, Proxima Centauri, which is only 4.22 light-years away (over twenty-four million miles), Alpha Centauri is the next closest star at 4.35 light years.

736 Q:
What are the twelve signs of the zodiac?

737 Q:
Match these superheroes with their everyday names.

Superman	Dr. Bruce Banner
Spiderman	Diana Prince
Captain Marvel	Billy Batson
Batman	Peter Parker
Incredible Hulk	Clark Kent
Wonder Woman	Bruce Wayne

738 Q:
We all know Trigger was the name of Roy Rogers's horse, but what was the name of Gene Autry's horse?

739 Q:
How fast can a rhinoceros run?

740 Q:
How many horns does a rhinoceros have?

736 A: Aries (March 21–April 19); Taurus (April 20–May 20); Gemini (May 21–June 21); Cancer (June 22–July 22); Leo (July 23–August 22); Virgo (August 23–September 22); Libra (September 23–October 23); Scorpio (October 24–November 21); Sagittarius (November 22–December 21); Capricorn (December 22–January 19); Aquarius (January 20–February 18); Pisces (February 19–March 20).

737 A:
Superman = Clark Kent
Spiderman = Peter Parker
Captain Marvel = Billy Batson
Batman = Bruce Wayne
The Incredible Hulk = Dr. Bruce Banner
Wonder Woman = Diana Prince

738 A: Champion, who lived to the age of forty-one.

739 A: These brawny beasts can charge at speeds of up to thirty miles per hour. A cornered rhino attacks with its horn.

740 A: There are actually five different kinds of rhinoceroses: the African white, the African black, and the Sumatran rhinoceroses all have two horns; the Indian and the Javan rhinoceroses both have only one horn.

741 Q:
When was the first Harley-Davidson motorcycle made?

742 Q:
How old is the Indian Motorcycle Company?

743 Q:
"Have you no sense of decency, sir?" Who made this outraged plea?

744 Q:
How was Bermuda discovered?

741 A: William S. Harley and Arthur Davidson, both in their early twenties, produced the first Harley-Davidson motorcycles in Milwaukee in 1903. The factory in which they originally worked was a rustic wooden shed with the words "Harley-Davidson Motor Company" scrawled on the door.

742 A: George Hendee and Oscar Hedstrom founded the cycle enterprise in Springfield, Massachusetts, in 1901, predating Harley-Davidson by two years. While the original company ceased operations in 1953, the name lives on in an Iowa-based firm that produces Indian motorcycles in limited numbers.

743 A: With these words, Army counsel Joseph Welch challenged Senator Joseph McCarthy during congressional hearings inspired by the latter's charge of Communist subversion in the American military. These televised interrogations helped cause McCarthy's downfall.

744 A: In 1609, while attempting to go to Jamestown, Virginia, English settlers were shipwrecked off Bermuda. After washing up on the shores, they pragmatically claimed the island as a colony for England. Shakespeare used this story as his source material for *The Tempest* (1611).

745 Q:
Who was the founder of the sect called the Shakers?

746 Q:
When was the Biedermeier style of furniture introduced? How did it get its name?

747 Q:
Who played Rhett Butler in the 1994 TV miniseries *Scarlett,* which was a sequel to 1939's *Gone With the Wind*? Who played Scarlett?

748 Q:
In the film *Casablanca,* who played and sang the song "As Time Goes By"?

749 Q:
What film was the first mass-release "scratch-and-sniff" movie?

750 Q:
The Godfather won the Best Picture Oscar in 1972. Did *The Godfather II* repeat that feat?

745 A: Mother Ann Lee is generally regarded as the founder of the Shakers, who received the nickname "Shaking Quakers" because of their religious dancing. In 1774, Lee and her little group moved from England to America, where they lived celibate lives in rural communes, their survival assured only by converts. Today, they are probably best remembered for their spare, well-crafted wooden furniture.

746 A: Biedermeier furniture, which has been described as utilitarian furniture for the bourgeoisie, was popular in Germany from around 1815 to 1850. There was a comic satirical character called "Papa Biedermeier," and the name was disparagingly applied to this new style for being hopelessly bourgeois.

747 A: Timothy Dalton played Rhett, with Joanne Whaley as Scarlett. In the original 1939 film, Clark Gable was Rhett, and Vivien Leigh was Scarlett.

748 A: Dooley Wilson was Sam, who famously played it again. The 1942 film starred Humphrey Bogart and Ingrid Bergman.

749 A: John Waters introduced the innovative "Odorama" in the film *Polyester* (1981), which starred Divine as a suburban housewife. Heartthrob Tab Hunter was in the supporting cast.

750 A: Yes, the film snagged 1974 honors.

751 Q:
What was the only X-rated film to win the Academy Award for Best Picture?

752 Q:
Where is the longest mountain range in the world?

753 Q:
What is the largest lake in South America?

754 Q:
What is the largest freshwater lake in South America?

755 Q:
Which South American country is the largest in terms of land area?

756 Q:
What South American nation has the largest population?

751 A: 1969's *Midnight Cowboy* is the only film with that adult rating to win Best Picture; it was later re-edited for an R rating. The film, which starred Dustin Hoffman and Jon Voight, also won the Oscar for Best Director for John Schlesinger, and Best Screenplay for Waldo Salt.

752 A: The world's longest mountain range, the Andes mountain system, stretches over 5,000 miles through seven South American countries: Argentina, Chile, Bolivia, Peru, Ecuador, Colombia, and Venezuela. The Falkland Islands and a part of Antarctica are actually continuations of the Andes.

753 A: Lake Maracaibo, a brackish lake in Venezuela, has a surface area of approximately 5,100 square miles.

754 A: Lake Titicaca, which is in the Andes Mountains on the boundary of Bolivia and Peru, has a surface area of 3,141 square miles. At 12,500 feet above sea level, it is also the world's highest large lake.

755 A: Brazil, which has 3,286,469 square miles, occupies nearly half of the continent.

756 A: The Federative Republic of Brazil, with an estimated population of over 192 million people, according to a 2011 estimate.

757 Q:
Match the capital cities with their countries.

Argentina	. . . .	Caracas
Peru	. . . .	Santiago
Chile	. . . .	Lima
Venezuela	. . . .	Bogotá
Colombia	. . . .	Buenos Aires

758 Q:
Are people's tastes in books linked with the kinds of dreams they have?

759 Q:
Who was John Newbery and what are his two claims to fame?

760 Q:
Who was Randolph Caldecott?

761 Q:
One president dismissed another as "a barbarian who could not write a sentence of grammar and hardly could spell his own name." Who was the accuser and who was his White House target?

757 A:
Argentina = Buenos Aires
Peru = Lima
Chile = Santiago
Venezuela = Caracas
Colombia = Bogotá

758 A: According to a University of Wales study, yes. Tabulating results from 10,000 people, the researchers found that adults who read fiction have stranger dreams than readers of nonfiction. They also learned that fantasy readers have the most nightmares, and romance readers have dreams with great emotional intensity. This was the first major study of the relationship between the choice of reading material and the content of dreams.

759 A: John Newbery (1713–67) was an English bookseller and publisher who was the first publisher of books for children. Since 1921, the American Library Association has given an annual John Newbery Medal award to the most distinguished children's book of the year.

760 A: Randolph Caldecott (1846–86) was a British painter and illustrator of children's books. Since 1938, the American Library Association has given the Caldecott Medal to the illustrator of the best U.S. children's picture book of the year.

761 A: As you can deduce from this quotation, John Quincy Adams had few kind words about Andrew Jackson.

762 Q:

What is the name of the 1958 film starring Andy Griffith in the role of a simple-minded hillbilly who has been drafted into the Air Force?

763 Q:

What are the first names of the members of the following TV families: the Cleavers, the Partridge Family, the Huxtables, and the Simpsons?

764 Q:

Where did Matt Groening, the creator of *The Simpsons*, get the names for his TV family?

765 Q:

What was the name of Wally Cleaver's best friend in *Leave It to Beaver* (1957–63)?

766 Q:

What kind of work did Wally and Beaver's dad do?

762 A: *No Time for Sergeants*. The light-hearted film, which had been a Broadway play, was directed by Mervyn LeRoy. Griffith played Will Stockdale; Nick Adams and Don Knotts also appeared in the movie. Both the play and movie were based on the novel *No Time For Sergeants* by Mac Hyman, first published in 1954.

763 A: The Cleavers: Ward, June, Wally, and Theodore (Beaver). The Partridges: Shirley, Keith, Laurie, Danny, Christopher, and Tracy. The Huxtables: Heathcliff (Cliff), Clair, Theodore (Theo), Denise, Sondra, Vanessa, Rudy, and (later) Olivia. The Simpsons: Homer, Marge, Bart, Lisa, and baby Maggie.

764 A: Groening playfully named them after his own relatives: Groening's father is named Homer, his mother is Marge, and he has two sisters, Lisa and Maggie. Bart, however, is an anagram of "brat."

765 A: Eddie Haskell, known best for his obsequious attitude toward persons of authority, was the best friend of Wally, Beaver's older brother.

766 A: Ward Cleaver constantly wore a suit, went to an office somewhere in town (sometimes even going to work on Saturday), and had a secretary. The family seemed to have a comfortable middle-class lifestyle—but we never found out what business Ward was in.

767 Q:
Sam Cooke had many hit records in the 1950s and '60s, including "You Send Me," "A Change Is Gonna Come," and "Twistin' the Night Away." Before becoming famous as a pop singer, this short-lived Mississippian was a member of what gospel group?

768 Q:
In what year was Elvis Presley drafted into the U.S. Army?

769 Q:
Under what name did Ronnie Hawkins's back-up band, the Hawks, become famous?

770 Q:
When and where was the first Woodstock Festival held?

771 Q:
What three popular recording stars were killed in a plane crash on February 3, 1959, after performing in Clear Lake, Iowa?

772 Q:
Who was the inventor of the slot machine?

773 Q:
How did the American game of poker originate?

767 A: Between 1951 and 1956, Sam Cooke was the lead singer of the Soul Stirrers.

768 A: 1958. Presley entered the U.S. Army on March 24 of that year, and left active duty on March 5, 1960. For most of his deployment, he was stationed in Germany.

769 A: The Band. After playing with Hawkins, they became a back-up band for Bob Dylan. In 1966, the Band released their first album, *Music from Big Pink*.

770 A: August 15–17, 1969, in Bethel, New York. Approximately 400,000 festival-goers showed up.

771 A: Buddy Holly, Ritchie Valens, and the Big Bopper (Jiles Perry Richardson). Don McLean's 1971 song "American Pie" touches on this tragic event.

772 A: Although there were already some mechanical poker machines around, Bavarian immigrant Charles A. Fey created the first Liberty Bell slot machine in his San Francisco basement in 1899. The top winning combination was three bells in a row.

773 A: As early as the Renaissance, Italians played a card game called primero. In this diversion, each player received four cards and could bid, stake, or pass. The game evolved over the years; one version was a French card game called poque, the name of which was Americanized to poker. It is also claimed that poker was influenced by a similar Persian card game called as-nas.

774 Q:

What is the highest-ranking winning hand in modern-day poker in the U.S.?

775 Q:

What hand in poker is known as a "dead man's hand"?

776 Q:

What is the function of the honeycomb of bumps on an alligator's jaw?

777 Q:

What type of insect is kept in apiaries?

778 Q:

What is soul singer Barry White's important role in helping the environmental movement?

774 A: A royal flush: ace, king, queen, jack, and ten of the same suit. In case of a tie, the suits are ranked alphabetically: clubs, diamonds, hearts, and spades. However, a royal flush is a once-in-a-lifetime event, so it is highly improbable that two hands in the same game would be royal flushes.

775 A: On August 2, 1876, Wild Bill Hickok was shot in the back of the head by Jack McCall in a saloon in Deadwood, South Dakota. When he met his fate, the gunslinger was holding a pair of aces and a pair of eights, which became known as a "dead man's hand."

776 A: As reported in *Nature* magazine, the bumps that cover an alligator's jaw are sensors so sensitive that they can detect ripples from a single drop of water. Alligators can pinpoint the splashes in the water and stay alert to danger, even while snoozing in the sun.

777 A: Bees are kept in apiaries, the structures where they build their hives.

778 A: Researchers in Birmingham, England, discovered that lobsters reproduced more rapidly when Barry White's soul sounds were piped into the aquarium. Now, researchers attempting to get great white sharks to breed in captivity are going to use "Can't Get Enough of Your Love, Babe," "You're the First, the Last, My Everything," and other Barry White hits to help set the romantic mood.

779 Q:
What is a mink?

780 Q:
What is an ermine?

781 Q:
Throughout the 1800s, Rocky Mountain locusts periodically ravaged farm fields in the Midwest and western United States, sometimes in clouds hundreds of miles long. Then, they seemed to disappear. What happened to them?

782 Q:
What body of water has the distinction of having the world's highest tides?

779 A: This highly prized creature is a semiaquatic carnivorous mammal of the weasel family. The mink originated in North America, but is now distributed all over the world. Known for their beautiful sleek fur, minks are often farmed. They swim very well and like to eat small fish, eggs, birds, and small mammals.

780 A: Classified as one of the hundred worst invasive species, the ermine is a short-tailed weasel whose fur turns white in the winter. Mice are its main food, but it also eats small mammals and birds. *Ermine* is also the name for the highly valued winter-white fur of both the ermine and the long-tailed weasel. In the Middle Ages, only royalty wore white fur; the black-tipped tails were used as the traditional trim on royal robes.

781 A: They appear to be extinct; the last live Rocky Mountain locust was collected more than a century ago. Researchers believe that changes to their habitat caused their demise: farming the land in the valleys where they lived, the destruction of locust eggs by turning the soil, and the introduction of new plants and animals. Recently, researchers have found intact locust bodies in glaciers, which they will use for further studies.

782 A: The Bay of Fundy, which is an arm of the northern Atlantic Ocean between New Brunswick and Nova Scotia, has the greatest fluctuation in tide levels—as much as seventy feet!

783 Q:
What is a riptide?

784 Q:
Where is the Bering Sea?

785 Q:
Who holds the record for greatest number of years hosting a television talk show?

786 Q:
What show lays claim to being the longest-running network television program?

787 Q:
What show was television's longest running western?

783 A: These dangerous strong currents are formed when water that is pushed up on shore cannot easily return, and becomes trapped inside the break near shore. As gravity pulls the water back toward the sea, a river-like current develops, eroding a channel, and creating what is known as a rip current, or riptide. It is estimated that 80 percent of the rescues by lifeguards at America's beaches are due to people being caught in rip currents.

784 A: This body of water is the extreme northern arm of the Pacific Ocean that separates Alaska (U.S.) from Siberia (Russia). The Bering Sea was named for Danish explorer Vitus Jonassen Bering (1681–1741), who discovered the straits while in the service of Russia.

785 A: It is believed to be Joe Franklin. Beginning in the 1950s, *The Joe Franklin Show* ran on New York television for more than forty consecutive years! Joe, who also has had a radio show, claims to have interviewed a few hundred thousand guests, including such stars as Bing Crosby, Bill Cosby, and John Lennon, as well as many, many relatively unknown denizens of showbiz.

786 A: NBC's *Meet the Press*, now hosted by David Gregory; it has been on the air continuously since 1947.

787 A: *Gunsmoke* (1955–75), starring James Arness as Marshall Matt Dillon.

788 Q:
Set in the fictional town of Springfield, this show is credited by Guinness World Records as the longest running drama in television history. Can you name it?

789 Q:
Where did M&Ms get their name?

790 Q:
As of the 2010 census, where is the population center of the United States?

791 Q:
According to recent estimates, what percentage of the residents of New York City was foreign-born?

792 Q:
Who was the first president to be born west of the Mississippi? Who was the most recent?

788 A: *Guiding Light* debuted on CBS television on June 30, 1952, and continued running until its final show on September 18, 2009.

789 A: From the last names of candy company owners Forrest Mars and Bruce Murrie. Introduced in 1941, these plain chocolate candies became a favorite of American GIs serving in World War II. Why? Because M&Ms melted in their mouths, not in their hands.

790 A: Continuing a ninety-year-long trend, the center of the population has moved west—to Texas County in south-central Missouri.

791 A: Thirty-six percent of Big Apple residents—approximately 2.9 million New Yorkers—were born outside of the United States.

792 A: Eight presidents were born west of the Mississippi River. The first one was the thirty-first president, Herbert Hoover, who was born in West Branch, Iowa. Then followed Presidents Truman (Lamar, Missouri), Eisenhower (Denison, Texas), Johnson (near Stonewall, Texas), Nixon (Yorba Linda, California), Ford (Omaha, Nebraska), and Clinton (Hope, Arkansas). Most recently, Barack Obama earns that distinction by having been born in Honolulu, Hawaii.

793 Q:
What is the smallest state west of the Mississippi River?

794 Q:
Which U.S. state contains the most square miles of inland water?

795 Q:
When was Kleenex first introduced?

796 Q:
When were Scott paper towels first sold?

797 Q:
What percentage of eighteen- to thirty-four-year-olds drink alcohol?

798 Q:
Speaking of overindulgence, what team has invented a high-tech beer glass that, when empty, automatically orders another drink?

799 Q:
Which best-selling author was once a Democratic state legislator from Mississippi?

793 A: Hawaii, with a total land area of 6,470 square miles.

794 A: With its 20,171 square miles of inland water, Alaska qualifies for that honor. In fact, there are more than three million lakes in the state. The largest, Lake Iliamna, is the size of Connecticut.

795 A: Kleenex Cold Cream Remover tissues came out in 1924, but it was not until 1930 that Kleenex was marketed as a disposable handkerchief. In 1930, Kleenex changed its name to Kleenex Facial Tissue.

796 A: In 1907 the Scott brothers of Philadelphia introduced SANITOWEL paper towels, aimed at the institutional market. In 1931, Scott introduced the first paper towel for use in the kitchen.

797 A: According to a 2010 Gallup survey, 72 percent of that age group drink. For those over fifty-five, the percentage slips to 59.

798 A: As reported in *New Scientist*, a team from Mitsubishi Electric Research Laboratories has developed a prototype for a beer glass that is fitted with a radio-frequency coil that emits a signal to the bartender when the glass is empty.

799 A: John Grisham is a lawyer who is also the author of many top-selling titles, including *The Firm*, *A Time to Kill*, *The Pelican Brief*, *The Summons*, *Theodore Boone*, *The Litigators*, and *The Confession*.

800 Q:

Which irrepressible chef and television personality hosted the TV cooking show *The French Chef*? (Hint: She was also the author of numerous best-selling cookbooks.)

801 Q:

What South American novelist and short-story writer won the Nobel Prize in Literature in 1982?

802 Q:

Ferdinand Magellan named the Pacific Ocean, and had the Straits of Magellan named for him. In what year did the Portuguese explorer begin the first circumnavigation of the globe? When did he complete the voyage?

803 Q:

On March 30, 2002, Britain's Queen Mother died at the age of 101. Who was she and why was she not the British queen?

804 Q:

Where is George Washington buried?

805 Q:

Where is Abraham Lincoln buried?

800 A: Julia Child. Her liveliness and cooking skills made her a hit onscreen and off. Her first best seller was *Mastering the Art of French Cooking*, written with Simone Beck and Louisette Bertholle.

801 A: Gabriel García Márquez, whose most famous work is *One Hundred Years of Solitude*, was the first Colombian author to receive the coveted prize. His writing style has been described as "magical realism."

802 A: In 1519. He did not live to complete his voyage, having been killed in a 1521 uprising by locals in the Philippines. His crew continued the ship's voyage around the world, finishing in 1522.

803 A: The Queen Mother, born as Lady Elizabeth Angela Marguerite Bowes-Lyon, was the mother of Queen Elizabeth II. Married to King George VI, she served as queen consort until his death in 1952. On the coronation of her daughter a year later, she became the dowager queen, or the Queen Mother. (Likewise, the husband of Queen Elizabeth II, Prince Philip, the Duke of Edinburgh, is not a king but a prince consort.)

804 A: Following his wishes, Washington was buried on his Mount Vernon estate in Virginia, after his death on December 14, 1799.

805 A: Lincoln was buried in his hometown of Springfield, Illinois. His remains rest there at the Old Ridge Cemetery.

806 Q:
How many states' names are spelled with only one vowel, such as Alabama? Can you name them?

807 Q:
Are the names of any states spelled with a single consonant?

808 Q:
How many states have a name of one syllable?

809 Q:
Do any states have rectangular shapes?

810 Q:
How many states border the Great Lakes? Name them.

811 Q:
What former Brooklyn Dodgers first baseman went on to star in his own television western?

812 Q:
When USSR leader Leonid Brezhnev visited the United States in the early 1970s, the White House staff asked him if there were any Americans he would like to meet. What television star did Brezhnev want to meet?

806 A: Seven: Alabama, Alaska, Arkansas, Kansas, Maryland, Mississippi, Tennessee, and New Jersey.

807 A: Only two: Ohio, Iowa.

808 A: Maine is the only state with a one-syllable moniker.

809 A: There are two rectangular states—Colorado and Wyoming. Residents of the Dakotas, Kansas, and Pennsylvania might disagree, but these states don't quite qualify.

810 A: Eight states: Minnesota, Wisconsin, Illinois, Indiana, Michigan, Ohio, Pennsylvania, and New York.

811 A: Chuck Connors played major league baseball in 1949 and 1950 before moving to Hollywood. As Luke McCain, he was the star of ABC's popular western series *The Rifleman*, which debuted in 1958.

812 A: Chuck Connors. *The Rifleman* was Breshnev's favorite American show.

813 Q:

What actor played the lead in the television series *The Cisco Kid* (1950–56)? What was the name of Cisco's sidekick?

814 Q:

What were the names of the two lead characters on NBC's *The Man from U.N.C.L.E.* (1964–68)? Who played them?

815 Q:

What is a tarantula?

816 Q:

What is the tarantella?

817 Q:

What is John Wayne's birth name?

818 Q:

Name the first actress to play M in a Bond film.

819 Q:

Which Bond girl also starred in a movie with Elvis Presley? What movie did Elvis and the Bond girl make together?

820 Q:

Who played "Deep Throat" in the 1976 film *All the President's Men*?

813 A: Duncan Renaldo played the Hispanic Cisco on television and in movies, but he was actually Romanian-born. Pancho, his constant companion, was portrayed by Leo Carrillo. At the end of each program, they used to remark to each other, "Oh, Cisco!" "Oh, Pancho!"

814 A: International agents Napoleon Solo and Ilya Kuryakin were played, respectively, by Robert Vaughn and David McCallum.

815 A: This dreaded creepy crawler is a large, hairy spider that eats insects and small vertebrates. Despite folklore, its venom seldom has a serious effect on humans.

816 A: A folk dance of southern Italy, in 6/8 time.

817 A: Marion Michael Morison.

818 A: Dame Judi Dench, in *Goldeneye* (1995).

819 A: Ursula Andress. *Fun in Acapulco* (1963).

820 A: Hal Holbrook.

821 Q:

Who provided the voice of the baby in *Look Who's Talking* (1989)?

822 Q:

How did artist Vincent van Gogh die?

823 Q:

To which faraway place did French artist Gauguin move?

824 Q:

Who played Gauguin in the 1956 movie *Lust for Life*, which starred Kirk Douglas as Vincent van Gogh?

825 Q:

What American impressionist artist and printmaker living in Paris was best known for her paintings of mothers and children?

826 Q:

What is the name of the show that served as the introduction of modern art to the United States?

827 Q:

The destruction of what Spanish city in 1937 during the Spanish Civil War inspired a famous painting by Pablo Picasso?

821 A: Bruce Willis.

822 A: After cutting off his left ear in 1889, the haunted Dutch painter died from a self-inflicted gunshot wound the following year, but some recent accounts suggest he could have been killed.

823 A: Van Gogh's friend, Paul Eugene Henri Gauguin (1848–1903), went to Tahiti and the Marquesas in 1892.

824 A: Anthony Quinn.

825 A: Mary Cassatt (1844–1926), who played an important role in introducing modern art to the U.S.

826 A: The New York Armory Show, officially called the International Exhibition of Modern Art, opened on February 17, 1913.

827 A: Guernica.

828 Q:

Match these historic American ballparks with the cities where they once existed.

1. Tiger Stadium . . . . a. St. Louis
2. Crosley Field . . . . b. Philadelphia
3. Sportsman's Park . . . . c. New York
4. Polo Grounds . . . . d. Detroit
5. Shibe Park . . . . e. Cincinnati

829 Q:

When was Yankee Stadium first opened? Where had the Bronx Bombers played previously?

830 Q:

What baseball team was known as the Washington Senators from 1901 to 1960?

831 Q:

How old is Smokey Bear?

828 A:

1.—**d.** Tiger Stadium opened in Detroit in 1912 as Novin Field, later becoming Tiger Stadium; it was home to the Tigers for eighty-eight seasons.

2.—**e.** Crosley Field was the home of the Cincinnati Reds from 1912 to 1970.

3.—**a.** Sportsman's Park in St. Louis was home to the Cardinals and the Browns for thirty-three years.

4.—**c.** The Polo Grounds were home to the New York Giants from 1911 to 1957; the Yankees and the Mets also played there for periods of time over the years.

5.—**b.** Shibe Park in Philadelphia closed in 1970; it had a thirty-four-foot-high right field wall.

829 A: The first game played at "the House That Ruth Built" was on April 18, 1923, against the Boston Red Sox. Before then, the team played at American League Park (1901–02), Hilltop Park (1903–12), and the Polo Grounds (1913–22).

830 A: The Minnesota Twins, who moved to Minnesota from Washington, D.C., in 1961.

831 A: In 1944, the U.S. Forest Service, in conjunction with the Advertising Council, authorized a poster by Albert Staehle of Smokey Bear (often called Smokey the Bear) as the symbol for fire prevention. Remember, kids: "Only You Can Prevent Forest Fires."

832 Q:
Who triumphed at the Bay of Pigs?

833 Q:
On the night of June 16–17, 1972, five men were arrested trying to bug the offices of the Democratic National Committee at the Watergate Hotel and Office Building. Who was the unlikely hero who pushed the first domino that brought down President Richard Nixon?

834 Q:
In the 1941 film *Citizen Kane*, who actually hears Charles Foster Kane utter his famous last word, "Rosebud"?

835 Q:
What, in fact, was Rosebud?

836 Q:
This actor appeared briefly as a reporter at the end of *Citizen Kane*. Smoking a pipe, he speaks only a few lines, but just a few years later, he went on to major film stardom. Name him.

837 Q:
How old was Orson Welles when he co-wrote, directed, and starred in *Citizen Kane* (1941)?

832 A: Certainly not the CIA-trained Cuban exiles who planned to invade Cuba and overthrow Communist Fidel Castro. On April 17, 1961, about 1,500 anti-Castro exiles, trained and armed by the United States, landed at the Bahía de Cochinos (Bay of Pigs) on the southern coast of Cuba. Almost from the start, the "invasion" was a fiasco.

833 A: Building security guard Frank Wills. This eagle-eyed hotel employee spotted a taped lock on a door. He removed the tape, but, when he passed by again about ten minutes later, a new piece had been put on. Wills then called the police.

834 A: Nobody. Kane utters the word when he's alone in his bedroom. The nurse enters his room after he drops the glass snow paperweight.

835 A: It was the name of Charles Foster Kane's childhood sled.

836 A: Alan Ladd.

837 A: Twenty-five.

838 Q:
What two countries' coastlines border the Bay of Biscay?

839 Q:
In what continents are the following countries: Bahrain, Suriname, Tunisia, Malawi, Latvia?

840 Q:
What is the name of the world's deepest lake?

841 Q:
What countries border Lake Victoria?

842 Q:
Which president described another U.S. chief as "a bewildered, confounded, and miserably perplexed man"?

843 Q:
Identify Europe's longest river.

844 Q:
Napoleon I was born on the island of Corsica in 1769. On what island did he die?

845 Q:
Where is Hispaniola?

838 A: France and Spain border this arm of the Atlantic Ocean.

839 A: The Kingdom of Bahrain is in the Persian Gulf (Asia); the Republic of Suriname is on the northern coast of South America, next to Guyana and above Brazil; the Republic of Tunisia is in northern Africa on the Mediterranean; the Republic of Malawi is in southeastern Africa, bordering Tanzania, Zambia, and Mozambique; the Republic of Latvia is in eastern Europe, on the Baltic Sea.

840 A: With a maximum depth of one mile, Russia's Lake Baikal, in Siberia, earns that superlative.

841 A: Uganda, Tanzania, and Kenya border the world's third-largest lake. Lake Victoria is the chief source of the Nile.

842 A: Abraham Lincoln typified James Polk in those words.

843 A: The Volga River is Europe's longest, flowing 2,290 miles from the Valdai Plateau northwest of Moscow to the Caspian Sea.

844 A: Napoleon died in exile on the island of St. Helena, in the southern Atlantic, in 1821. Earlier, Napoleon had been exiled on the island of Elba, from which he escaped.

845 A: Hispaniola is an island in the West Indies, just southeast of Cuba, comprising two nations: the Dominican Republic occupies its eastern two-thirds, and Haiti its western side.

846 Q:
On what island did Christopher Columbus first land on his voyage in 1492?

847 Q:
Where is Christopher Columbus buried?

848 Q:
When did the United States first begin using American dollars?

849 Q:
The roadrunner is the official bird of which state?

846 A: Although disputes remain, many believe that he first landed on Guanahani or Watling Island, a small island of the Bahamas. Whatever we now call it, the great explorer named the island San Salvador. On that first voyage, he also visited Cuba and Hispaniola.

847 A: Again, a matter of some controversy. Both Spain and the Dominican Republic claim to have his remains. After completing four voyages to the New World, Columbus died in 1506 in Spain, but he wished to be buried in the Americas. In the years since, his body was shipped around to various burial sites, and, because of a possible mix-up or deception, it is not certain exactly which remains are his. Recent DNA and other evidence seem to indicate, however, that the bone fragments in Seville, Spain, at least are authentic.

848 A: At the time of the American Revolution, the Spanish "pillar dollar" was the principal coin of commerce in the American colonies. Another widely distributed world currency was the German thaler. The Continental Congress established the dollar as the monetary unit of the United States on July 6, 1785, but the U.S. Mint was not created until 1792, with the passage of the Coinage Act.

849 A: This fast moving flier, not to be confused with his cartoon equivalent, is the official bird of the state of New Mexico; the state flower of the Land of Enchantment is the yucca.

850 Q:

What is the only mobile U.S. national monument?

851 Q:

Which state's capitol building is a scaled-down replica of the United States Capitol?

852 Q:

Who is credited with the invention of the earmuff?

853 Q:

Can you name the one presidential overnight guest who smoked a joint on the White House roof—and admitted it?

854 Q:

What city hosted the first modern-day Olympics?

855 Q:

How long did Walter Cronkite host the CBS *Evening News*? How did "the most trusted man in America" end every broadcast?

856 Q:

Name all the regular hosts of *The Tonight Show*.

850 A: San Francisco's cable cars.

851 A: The Arkansas State Capitol. No wonder Bill Clinton ran for President—he already knew the layout.

852 A: These effective head warmers were invented in 1873 in Maine by Chester Greenwood. Perhaps it should not surprise us that Pine Tree State was once known as the "Earmuff Capital of the World."

853 A: Willie Nelson toked a doobie while making an executive visit during the Carter administration.

854 A: The first modern-day Olympics, which were inspired by the ancient Greeks' Olympic games, took place in Athens, Greece, in 1896. In 2004, the Olympics returned to Athens.

855 A: Cronkite hosted the news program for almost twenty years, from 1962 until his retirement in 1981. His nightly sign-off was "and that's the way it is."

856 A: Steve Allen (beginning in 1954); Jack Paar (1957), Johnny Carson (1962), Jay Leno (1992), Conan O'Brien (2009), and Jay Leno again (2010).

857 Q:
Who was Mohamed Bouazizi, and how did this lowly fruit and vegetable vendor earn a place in history?

858 Q:
Where did *Murder, She Wrote*'s Jessica Fletcher live?

859 Q:
Where did Sheriff Andy Griffith live?

860 Q:
What future film director played Opie on *The Andy Griffith Show* (1960–68)?

861 Q:
What Oscar-winning movie director was a *Happy Days* regular?

862 Q:
On what unpublished play is *Casablanca* based?

857 A: In December of 2010, police confiscated the cart, scales, and produce of this twenty-six-year-old Tunisian. Gravely upset by the loss of the livelihood for himself and his extended family, he went to the local municipal building and set himself on fire in protest. He later died at a hospital, but news of the incident and subsequent demonstrations ignited the revolutions across North Africa and the Middle East now known as the Arab Spring.

858 A: Mystery writer and friendly sleuth Fletcher lived in Cabot Cove. By the evidence of the show, Cabot Cove must have had the nation's highest homicide rate from 1984 to 1996.

859 A: With his aunt Bea and his son, Opie, in hospitable Mayberry, North Carolina.

860 A: Ron Howard, whose directing credits include *Splash*, *Backdraft*, and *Apollo 13*.

861 A: Again, it's Ron Howard. As a young actor, he played the show's Richard Cunningham. His 2002 movie *A Beautiful Mind* earned him an Academy Award for Best Director.

862 A: *Everybody Comes to Rick's.* Murray Bennet and Joan Alison's play formed the basis of the 1942 cinema classic, but it wasn't actually produced as a play until 1991.

863 Q:
In what Hitchcock movie did Shirley MacLaine make her screen debut in 1955?

864 Q:
In the 1994 film *Quiz Show,* contestant Herbert Stempel (John Turturro) sacrifices his championship by missing what question?

865 Q:
What was Merle Oberon's real name?

866 Q:
On the Waterfront was set in Brooklyn, but where was it really filmed?

867 Q:
When was the height of "tulipomania" in the Netherlands?

868 Q:
Tulips are native to what area of the world?

869 Q:
What is the wettest spot in the United States of America?

870 Q:
How much rain does Death Valley get in a year?

863 A: *The Trouble with Harry.*

864 A: The name of the winner of the Best Picture Oscar for 1955. Although he knows the right answer, Stempel "guesses" *On the Waterfront* instead of the correct answer, *Marty.*

865 A: Estelle Merle O'Brien Thompson. The Tasmanian-born actress began her career as Queenie O'Brien.

866 A: Hoboken, New Jersey.

867 A: The height of "tulipomania" was from 1634–37; single tulip bulbs were selling for 3,000–4,500 guilders—the equivalent of $1,500–$2,250 dollars today. In 1637, the price of tulip bulbs crashed, thus reducing bulb speculators to poverty overnight.

868 A: Not Holland. The original homeland of most tulips was central Asia—the valleys of Tien Shan of the central Asian plains and the mountain ranges north of the Himalayas.

869 A: It's a tough call, but both Mount Waialeale on the Hawaiian island of Kauai and Big Bog on Maui receive around 400 inches of rain each year.

870 A: Only an average of one and a half inches of rain every year.

871 Q:
How much money do Americans spend on fast food each year?

872 Q:
How many karats is pure gold?

873 Q:
How old is Mr. Peanut?

874 Q:
Who described weeds as "a plant whose virtues have not yet been discovered"?

871 A: Approximately $130 billion per year. As recently as 1970, it was only $6 billion.

872 A: 24K.

873 A: The Planters' mascot first saw the light of advertising day in 1916. He was already an octogenarian when he first made it to the Macy's Thanksgiving Day Parade in 1997.

874 A: Ralph Waldo Emerson (1803–82).

875 Q:

Match the following familiar quotes to their authors.

1. "The best-laid schemes o' mice and men…"
2. "Heaven has no rage like love to hatred turned, nor hell a fury like a woman scorned."
3. "Oh what a tangled web we weave, when first we practice to deceive."
4. "A penny saved is a penny earned."
5. "Water, water everywhere… nor any drop to drink."
6. "To err is human; to forgive, divine."

a. Sir Walter Scott, Scottish novelist and poet (1771–1832)
b. Benjamin Franklin, American statesman and inventor (1706–90)
c. William Congreve, English playwright (1670–1729)
d. Alexander Pope, English poet (1688–1744)
e. Samuel Taylor Coleridge, English poet (1772–1834)
f. Robert Burns, Scottish poet (1759–96)

876 Q:

Who was Lady Godiva, and why is she famous?

877 Q:

The Amazon River, which is 4,000 miles long, is the largest river drainage system in South America. What is that continent's second-largest river drainage system?

875 A:
1.—**f.** Robert Burns, Scottish poet (1759–96)
2.—**c.** William Congreve, English playwright (1670–1729)
3.—**a.** Sir Walter Scott, Scottish novelist and poet (1771–1832)
4.—**b.** Benjamin Franklin, American statesman and inventor (1706–90)
5.—**e.** Samuel Taylor Coleridge, English poet (1772–1834)
6.—**d.** Alexander Pope, English poet (1688–1744)

876 A: According to legend, this eleventh-century English noblewoman obtained a reduction in the heavy taxes levied by her husband on the people of Coventry by consenting to ride naked through the streets on a white horse. Only one person disobeyed the orders not to watch her: "Peeping Tom" peered at her through a window.

877 A: The 2,400 mile-long Parana River, which is formed by the junction of the Paranaíba and the Rio Grande Rivers in Brazil, continues through Paraguay and Argentina, joining the Uruguay River in a huge delta at the head of the Río de la Plata.

878 Q:
What route was known as the Silk Road?

879 Q:
Where is the Extraterrestrial Highway?

880 Q:
Mount Everest is the tallest mountain in the world. For whom was it named?

881 Q:
What recent Japanese beauty trend might surprise many young American women?

878 A: The road, also called the Silk Route, was a series of land routes, over 3,750 miles long, that ran from the eastern Mediterranean to East Asia, and was used for trade and cross-cultural exchange. The Silk Road flourished from the second century BCE up until the second century CE, when the trade switched to sea routes.

879 A: This state highway, also known as Route 375, is not in outer space: It is 150 miles north of Las Vegas, near Area 51.

880 A: Though it is unknown if he ever actually saw it in person, Sir George Everest was the British superintendent of the trigonometric survey that led to the mountain being declared the world's highest peak. He was also surveyor-general of India and mapped all of the subcontinent in the nineteenth century. After his death, Peak XV, which Tibet-ans call Chomolungma (Sacred Mother of the Waters), was named in his honor.

881 A: In the West, crooked teeth are generally regarded as undesirable and often treated with braces, teeth-straightening surgery, and other orthodontic procedures, but in Japan, many women pay to have their straight teeth disarranged into "yaeba" or "double teeth," which they perceive as cute. This is not an isolated phenomenon; Japanese singers, actresses, and even manga and anime characters display faces that Ameri-cans might dismiss as snaggle-toothed.

882 Q:

Who played the title character on *The Phil Silvers Show (You'll Never Get Rich)?*

883 Q:

What was the unusual (some say advanced) plot device that George Burns employed on the 1950s *The George Burns & Gracie Allen Show?*

884 Q:

What was the name of the D.A. who lost every week to Perry Mason?

885 Q:

What future president hosted *Death Valley Days?*

886 Q:

When Coney Island's Luna Park burned down in 1944, people called it "Topsy's Revenge." Who was this movie star and why did he or she deserve payback?

887 Q:

When was paper invented?

882 A: Phil Silvers was Sergeant Bilko, the con man who ran the motor pool at Fort Baxter.

883 A: George was often seen in his den, puffing on his cigar as he watched and commented on the program we were watching.

884 A: D.A. Hamilton Burger, played by William Talman, was the chronically unlucky prosecutor on *Perry Mason* (1957–66).

885 A: Ronald Reagan. The 1964–65 stint was his last professional acting role before he turned his attention to politics.

886 A: Topsy was a female pachyderm who was sentenced to death after killing three humans. (In the captive animal's defense, it might be said that her final victim was an abusive trainer who tried to make her eat a lit cigarette.) In any case, the twenty-eight-year-old circus veteran received her fate at Luna Park on January 4, 1903. Inventor Thomas Edison actually captured the event on film, and his mercifully brief *Electrocuting an Elephant* became a nationwide hit later that year.

887 A: In 105 CE, historical records show that the invention of paper was reported to the Chinese emperor by Ts'ai Lun, an official of the imperial court. Recent archaeological investigations, however, place the actual invention of paper at least one hundred years earlier. Early Chinese paper was made from hemp.

888 Q:

Who patented the invention of the ballpoint pen in 1938?

889 Q:

Who played Che Guevara in the 1969 movie *Che*? And who played Fidel Castro?

890 Q:

Actor Michael Keaton changed his name because his original one was already taken. What was the redundant name?

891 Q:

Who was the original host of the 1980s music and dance show *Solid Gold*?

892 Q:

Who narrated *The Wonder Years* (1988–93)?

893 Q:

With a few exceptions (such as the Super Bowls) we now use Arabic numerals. When were Arabic numerals introduced into Europe?

894 Q:

Which United States mountain lays claim to having the world's windiest weather?

888 A: Hungarian inventor Laszlo Josef Biro, along with his brother George, patented the ballpoint pen. During World War II, the ballpoint pen was very popular with the military because of its toughness and its ability to write in airplanes at high altitudes.

889 A: Omar Sharif. Jack Palance.

890 A: Michael Douglas.

891 A: Dionne Warwick.

892 A: The voice of the older, wiser Kevin was supplied by Daniel Stern.

893 A: In 1202, by the Italian mathematician Leonardo of Pisa.

894 A: Antarctica is known for its bitter cold and high winds, but New Hampshire's Mount Washington, although not the tallest peak in the eastern United States, probably has the world's windiest weather—gusts recorded as high as 231 miles per hour.

895 Q:

Which veteran actor played Billy Bob Thornton's racist father in *Monster's Ball* and went on to become a fixture on *Everybody Loves Raymond*?

896 Q:

Only one Nobel Prize–winning economist became the subject of a movie. Can you name him?

897 Q:

How old is the Statue of Liberty?

898 Q:

Who was the first president of the American Federation of Labor?

899 Q:

What is the Walker Cup and what is its seldom-mentioned connection to a U.S. president?

900 Q:

What is the name of the "Michelin Man"?

901 Q:

When did Nelson Mandela become president of South Africa?

895 A: Peter Boyle.

896 A: John Nash, the focal point of *A Beautiful Mind*.

897 A: It depends how you measure its age. The statue was completed in France in 1884, then disassembled and shipped to New York City. President Grover Cleveland formally dedicated the gift on October 28, 1886.

898 A: Samuel Gompers (1850–1924), a leader in the cigar makers' union and a cofounder of the AFL.

899 A: This biannual male golf tournament takes its name from the trophy's donor, George Herbert Walker, the maternal great-grandfather of George Walker Bush, our forty-third president.

900 A: Bibendum. This cartoon creation, whose nickname is "Bib," has been part of the company's advertising arsenal since 1898.

901 A: On May 10, 1994, this revered activist was inaugurated after his party swept to victory in the nation's first free elections.

902 Q:

When did Ireland elect its first female president?

903 Q:

On what Pacific island were whales' teeth used as money until the late nineteenth century?

904 Q:

Which bird has the largest wingspan?

905 Q:

What snake is the longest snake?

906 Q:

Based in South Bend, Indiana, Studebaker was known as the only American manufacturer to successfully switch from the production of horse-drawn wagons to gasoline-powered vehicles. When was the last Studebaker car made?

907 Q:

In how many films did Basil Rathbone star as Sherlock Holmes?

908 Q:

What was the first Hollywood "talkie" (movie with synchronous spoken sound)? When was it released?

902 A: In 1990, when Mary Robinson won the post as an independent candidate.

903 A: Fiji.

904 A: The great white pelican, which has a wingspan of 141 inches.

905 A: The reticulated python is thirty-five feet long.

906 A: After a sixty-four-year history, the company made its last car in its Hamilton, Ontario, plant in March 1966.

907 A: Fourteen. He also portrayed Holmes in hundreds of radio broadcasts.

908 A: *The Jazz Singer*, starring Al Jolson, opened in theaters on October 6, 1927.

909 Q:

Robert Altman's film M*A*S*H* (1970) was turned into a very popular TV series. Only one actor reprised his role from the movie in the TV series. Name the actor and the character he played.

910 Q:

What was the name of the character played by Robert DeNiro in the 1976 film *Taxi Driver*?

911 Q:

What was the Coen brothers' first movie?

912 Q:

Which nation has won the most World Cups?

913 Q:

Where is the world's largest library?

914 Q:

James Michener's first published book was made into a musical and two movies. What are its titles?

915 Q:

How many wineries are in the United States? Which state ranks first in number?

909 A: Gary Burghoff played Radar O'Reilly.

910 A: Travis Bickle, a troubled Vietnam vet who drives a cab in New York City.

911 A: *Blood Simple* (1984).

912 A: Brazil, which won its fifth World Cup championship (soccer) in 2002. With four FIFA titles, Italy is close behind.

913 A: Washington, D.C. The United States Library of Congress, which was founded in 1800, has over 150 million books, magazines, and items of ephemera.

914 A: His short story collection *Tales of the South Pacific* (1947) became the hit Rodgers and Hammerstein musical *South Pacific* (1949), before becoming a movie in 1958 and a television movie in 2001.

915 A: More than 4,700 and the number continues to grow. Over 1.1 million acres in the U.S. are under vine. Among states, California is, by far, the most wine prolific.

916 Q:

For over a month, one painting at New York's Museum of Modern Art hung upside down before an attentive visitor pointed it out. What was the painting?

917 Q:

What school has won the most College World Series titles?

918 Q:

In what year did President Richard Nixon visit the People's Republic of China?

919 Q:

What is the world's largest volcanic island?

920 Q:

Which country is the world's greatest producer of gold?

921 Q:

Which state has the longest shoreline?

922 Q:

What location holds the world record for the greatest difference between mean temperatures in winter and summer?

923 Q:

Who famously said, "It's like déjà vu all over again"?

916 A: Henri Matisse's *Le Bateau*.

917 A: University of Southern California, with twelve baseball championships. But they haven't won since 2001, and LSU, Texas, and Arizona State seem to be closing their lead.

918 A: On February 21, 1972, Nixon stepped down from Air Force One to shake hands with Premier Chou En-lai.

919 A: Sumatra, in Indonesia, has several active volcanoes across its 171,060 square miles.

920 A: South Africa, which produces 442 tons of gold annually.

921 A: Alaska, with 33,904 miles of shoreline. Florida is in second place with 8,426 miles of shoreline.

922 A: Verkhoyansk, Russia, where the mean temperature is -56 degrees Fahrenheit in winter and 56.5 degrees Fahrenheit in summer—a difference of 115 degrees.

923 A: Philosopher-ballplayer Yogi Berra. He reportedly made the comment upon being fired as New York Yankees manager for the second time by George Steinbrenner.

924 Q:
Which country has the world's longest network of roads (both paved and unpaved)?

925 Q:
Who was America's first postmaster general?

926 Q:
What is the highest reliably reported temperature in the Western Hemisphere?

927 Q:
Who were the principal allies of the United States in the First World War (1914–18)?

928 Q:
When did Adolf Hitler come to power?

929 Q:
The United States exploded the first atomic bomb on July 16, 1945. When did the Soviet Union test its first atomic bomb?

930 Q:
When did Mao Zedong (Tse-Tung) begin his "Long March" in China?

924 A: The United States, with more than six million miles of roads. The People's Republic of China is second with nearly four million miles, and India is third with over three million.

925 A: Benjamin Franklin. In 1775, the Continental Congress appointed him to the new post.

926 A: On July 10, 1913, a temperature of 134 degrees Fahrenheit was recorded at the aptly named Furnace Creek in California's Death Valley.

927 A: The United States fought with Britain, France, and Russia against Germany, the Austro-Hungarian Empire, and Turkey. The U.S. entered the war in 1917.

928 A: The Nazi leader became chancellor of Germany in January 1933, and, after eliminating his opposition and consolidating his power, was able to exercise dictatorial control in Germany until his suicide in a bunker in 1945.

929 A: The Soviet Union tested its first nuclear device on September 23, 1949.

930 A: On October 21, 1934, the Chinese Communist Red Army began the "Long March" of six thousand miles from Kiangsi to Yan'an. They reached their destination 368 days later, but not before one-third of the marchers had been killed along the way in battles with the Nationalist forces. This march saved the Communist movement from defeat.

931 Q:

What political leader delivered the famous 1946 "Iron Curtain" speech in Fulton, Missouri?

932 Q:

What is the chemical composition of the sun?

933 Q:

What is the most common word in the English language?

934 Q:

What famous pop artist of the 1960s made a 1985 guest appearance on *Love Point*?

935 Q:

What television role made Tony Danza famous?

936 Q:

Before becoming a movie megastar, Jim Carrey had a part on what TV show?

937 Q:

What was the name of "the love boat"?

938 Q:

What is the longest bone in the human body?

931 A: Despite the location, it wasn't Show-Me-State native and sitting U.S. president Harry Truman. It was Sir Winston Churchill who made the speech that demarked the coming international confrontation. The British prime minister was in Fulton to accept an honorary degree at Westminster College.

932 A: Hydrogen and helium make up over 99 percent of the sun.

933 A: "The."

934 A: Andy Warhol.

935 A: His portrayal of Tony Banta on *Taxi* (1978–83), a sitcom set in the garage of the fictional Sunshine Cab Company. This series also starred Danny DeVito, Judd Hirsch, Marilu Henner, Andy Kaufman, and Carol Kane.

936 A: *In Living Color* (1990–94), which starred Keenen Ivory Wayans.

937 A: The amorous ship was the *Pacific Princess*.

938 A: The femur, more commonly known as the thighbone, has the longest average length of any bone in the human body—almost twenty inches.

939 Q:
What living creature has the most legs?

940 Q:
What is the longest-running magazine in the United States?

941 Q:
What was the date on the first issue of *Playboy*? Who was the first centerfold?

942 Q:
Who was the oldest astronaut to go into space?

943 Q:
When was the first solo, nonstop transatlantic flight made?

944 Q:
In what year did Pan American Airways begin regular transpacific air service?

945 Q:
Who wrote the Pledge of Allegiance?

939 A: With its 750 appendages, the millipede.

940 A: *Scientific American*, which was founded in 1845.

941 A: There was no date. Marilyn Monroe was the first centerfold. In November 1953, when Hugh Hefner first published his magazine, he wasn't certain that there would ever be a second issue, so he left the issue dateless—a problem that Ms. Monroe seldom faced.

942 A: When astronaut John Glenn, Jr., returned to space on October 29, 1998, he earned that niche in history. At the time, he was seventy-seven years old.

943 A: In 1927, Charles A. Lindbergh flew his single engine monoplane, the Spirit of St. Louis, to Paris. He covered the 3,600 miles in thirty-three hours and twenty-nine minutes.

944 A: In 1935, Pan Am flew from San Francisco to Manila.

945 A: In 1892, Baptist minister and youth magazine editor Frances Bellamy wrote a twenty-one-word pledge that became widely used in schools. Since then, the Pledge of Allegiance has grown by ten words, its most famous addition being 1954's "under God."

946 Q:
1958 was the first year the recording industry gave out Grammy Awards. What record won the award for Best Rhythm and Blues Performance that year?

947 Q:
How did Gouda get its name?

948 Q:
Where was the world's first roller coaster erected?

949 Q:
Turin's Juventus F.C. easily qualifies as Italy's most successful soccer team with thirty league titles, but official records tally only twenty-eight. Why the discrepancy?

950 Q:
Which mammal has the longest gestation period?

951 Q:
Where was the potato first cultivated?

952 Q:
Who invented the Burbank potato?

946 A: *Tequila* by the Champs.

947 A: From its place of origin, the city of Gouda in the Netherlands.

948 A: In Coney Island, of course. LaMarcus Thompson's 1884 Switchback Railway had some ancestors, but he deserves credit for originating an amusement ride that still excites millions.

949 A: This national treasure was deeply implicated in the 2006 "Calciopoli" scandal. Convicted of rigging matches by selecting favorable referees, Juventus was stripped of its two most recent titles, but by 2011–12, the Italian favorite was back in the saddle again.

950 A: The African elephant, the world's largest land animal, has a gestation period (the time between fertilization and birth) of approximately 650 days.

951 A: This starchy, edible tuber was first cultivated in the Andean region of South America by the native population. Spanish explorers took the potato back to Spain in the middle of the sixteenth century, and from there it spread to the rest of Europe.

952 A: Luther Burbank (1849–1926) developed more than eight hundred varieties of plants, including his signature 1871 potato. Apparently, he didn't think much of his discovery: He sold the rights to the Burbank potato for only $150.

953 Q:
The worst maritime disaster in history became the subject of a novel by a Nobel Prize–winning author. Can you describe the incident and name the novel?

954 Q:
At what location did the Union Pacific Railroad meet the Central Pacific for the completion of the transcontinental railroad?

955 Q:
Where was the world's oldest living plant discovered, and how old is it?

956 Q:
What Academy Award–winning actor studied medicine at the University of California?

957 Q:
Lucille LeSueur is the real name of what legendary Hollywood actress?

958 Q:
Caryn Johnson is the birth name of what famous comedienne and actress?

953 A: In January 1945, just months before the end of the European war, the German cruise ship *Wilhelm Gustloff* was hit and sunk off the coast of Gdansk. Approximately 7,500 people perished, most of them refugees fleeing the Russian army offensive. German novelist Günter Grass, who grew up in the port city, wrote about the catastrophe in *Crabwalk*.

954 A: The tracks of the two railroads converged at Promontory Point, Utah. The Union Pacific had built 1,086 miles of track; the Central Pacific laid down the remaining 689.

955 A: The "King Clone" creosote bush of the Mojave Desert is estimated to be 11,700 years old.

956 A: Gregory Peck, who won the Best Actor Oscar for the 1962 film *To Kill A Mockingbird*.

957 A: Joan Crawford.

958 A: Whoopi Goldberg.

959 Q:
Name Grace Kelly's last movie before becoming princess of Monaco.

960 Q:
When and where did Walt Disney open his first amusement park?

961 Q:
In what year did Walt Disney World in Orlando open?

962 Q:
When did the last singing castrato die?

963 Q:
Why are the hottest days of summer called "the dog days"?

964 Q:
What is the name of the newspaper where Peter Parker gets a job in *Spider-Man*?

965 Q:
In the 2002 smash-hit movie *Spider-Man*, Peter Parker enters a wrestling match to earn some extra cash. What's the name of the wrestler he goes up against and the real professional wrestler who plays this meanie?

959 A: *High Society* (1956).

960 A: Disneyland opened on July 18, 1955, in Anaheim, California.

961 A: The ultimate amusement park first welcomed visitors in 1971.

962 A: Alessandro Moreschi, the last known castrato, died at the age of sixty-three on April 21, 1922, more than half a century after the Italian government made such castration illegal. He had been a member of the Sistine choir. The practice of castrating boys between the ages of six and eight to preserve the clear tone of voice began in the mid-sixteenth century.

963 A: Ancient Romans bestowed the name because the hottest summer days occur near the time of the year when Sirius, the dog star, and the Sun most closely converge. In early centuries, superstitious ancients even sacrificed a brown dog each year as the temperatures rose precipitously.

964 A: *The Daily Bugle.*

965 A: Bonesaw McGraw is played by Randy "Macho Man" Savage.

966 Q:

The ring announcer at that wrestling match has appeared in several of *Spider-Man* director Sam Raimi's films. What is this actor's name? What is the name of the first Sam Raimi feature film he appeared in?

967 Q:

What player became the first African-American NBA coach?

968 Q:

Who became the first African-American manager in major league baseball?

969 Q:

Who was the first African-American major league umpire?

970 Q:

Only one player in major league history has hit three home runs on his birthday. Who is this peerless birthday boy?

971 Q:

What city was the site of the treaty that ended the American Revolutionary War?

966 A: Bruce Campbell starred in Sam Raimi's cult classic *The Evil Dead* (1981).

967 A: Bill Russell became the player-coach of the Boston Celtics after the 1965–66 season.

968 A: Frank Robinson, who was Bill Russell's high school teammate in Oakland, gained that distinction when he accepted the Cleveland Indians managership in 1975.

969 A: Emmett Ashford spent fourteen years umpiring in the minor leagues before he got his big major league break in 1966.

970 A: On July 23, 2002, the Boston Red Sox's Nomar Garciaparra celebrated his twenty-ninth birthday by connecting for three home runs in the first game of a doubleheader. Two of his birthday bash homers were hit in a single inning!

971 A: Paris, France. The accord was signed on September 3, 1783.

972 Q:

Veteran actor Christopher Lee appeared in one of the biggest movies of 2001 and another mega-hit the next year. Name the two films and the two characters he portrayed.

973 Q:

This Oscar-winning supporting actor has appeared in numerous films, including *The Bourne Identity, American Beauty, Capote, The Town,* and *The Muppets.* Who is this versatile man?

974 Q:

What two-time Grammy Award–winning president can bench-press 200 pounds?

975 Q:

Can you name the major American author who wrote an episode of *McHale's Navy*?

976 Q:

Which actress/film director first achieved national exposure as the Coppertone baby?

977 Q:

What is the Kuiper belt?

972 A: Lee played the wicked Saruman in *The Lord of the Rings: The Fellowship of the Ring*. In 2002, Lee played the evil Count Dooku in *Star Wars Episode II: Attack of the Clones*.

973 A: Chris Cooper.

974 A: Barack Obama.

975 A: Joseph Heller wrote *Catch-22*, one of the most revered twentieth-century classics. Somewhat less known is Heller's script work on Ernest Borgnine's nautical TV comedy *McHale's Navy*, for which he used the pen name "Max Orange." Heller also helped write the James Bond spoof *Casino Royale* and the film *Sex and the Single Girl*.

976 A: Future star Jodie Foster was only three when she first appeared pig-tailed and bare-bottomed in Coppertone suntan lotion commercials.

977 A: It's not a midriff band; it is a ring of celestial bodies orbiting outside our solar system, beyond the farthest planets, Neptune and Pluto. Scientists believe that the Kuiper belt may be a source of comets.

978 Q:
What best-selling children's book author designed the costumes and settings for a New York City Ballet dance?

979 Q:
Did Apollo 14 astronaut Alan Shepard really drive a golf ball on the moon nearly half a mile?

980 Q:
Who holds television's kissing record?

981 Q:
What the "Imperfect Perfect Game"?

978 A: In 2003, Ian Falconer's colorful playing card–themed costumes and set brightened the new production of Peter Martins's choreography of Stravinsky's *Jeu de Cartes*. That premiere occurred just three years after Falconer's porcine prima ballerina Olivia first took the stage in a Caldecott Honor book.

979 A: No. According to duffer's legend, Shepard drove a ball 1,450 yards in the low gravity of the moon. That's about four times longer than Tiger Woods's best shot. The truth is more earthbound: Shepard's longest drive with a makeshift club went only a few hundred yards. That's not bad for a one-handed shot by a golfer in full astronaut's gear, but it's no world-record beater.

980 A: During his 1976–85 stint as the host of *Family Feud*, "Kissing Bandit" Richard Dawson bussed the lips of approximately 20,000 female guests.

981 A: On June 2, 2010, Detroit Tigers pitcher Armando Galarraga retired the first twenty-six Cleveland Indians he faced. His chances to become the twenty-first major league pitcher to pitch a perfect game were squelched when umpire Jim Joyce incorrectly called Jason Donald safe in what should have been the final out of the game. The circumstances of the so-called "28-out perfect game" brought out the best traits of the major participants: Umpire Joyce was abjectly apologetic, and Gallarraga was graciously forgiving.

982 Q:

In *Minority Report,* Tom Cruise doesn't exactly get a facelift, but he does have surgery to alter his appearance and aid his escape. What kind of surgery does he have?

983 Q:

Ben Affleck plays Jack Ryan in the 2002 movie *The Sum of All Fears.* Ryan has been portrayed by two other actors. Can you name the other two actors and also name the films featuring them as Jack Ryan?

984 Q:

When did Mr. Clean make his first television commercials?

985 Q:

Morris the Cat is the "spokesman" for what brand of cat food?

986 Q:

Retired science teacher Irv Gordon from Long Island recently set a motoring record with his cherry-red 1966 Volvo. What was it?

987 Q:

How long is the Trans-Siberian Railway?

982 A: In order to avoid the retinal identification machines, Cruise has surgery to replace his eyeballs. His sparkling blues are replaced with a pair that are deep brown.

983 A: Alec Baldwin was the first to play Jack Ryan on the big screen in *The Hunt for Red October*. Harrison Ford played Jack Ryan in two films: *Patriot Games* and *Clear and Present Danger*.

984 A: Mr. Clean products were introduced by Proctor & Gamble in 1958, and Mr. Clean, ahead of his time, completely bald and wearing an earring, was on TV from the beginning. He was listed as "one of the sexiest men alive" by *People* magazine in 1998.

985 A: Morris's career began in 1968 when 9Lives cat food discovered him in a Chicago-area animal shelter. Morris, who quickly became one of the leading TV personalities of the day, has also appeared in movies, magazines, and books.

986 A: Gordon holds the world record for the most miles driven in the same car; as of 2012, he's approaching three million. Gordon has also shipped his Volvo to Europe, where he did a 5,000-mile road trip, including a stop at Volvo headquarters in Sweden.

987 A: This historic span runs 5,777 miles from Moscow to Vladivostok and crosses seven time zones. Nearly the entire line is now electrified.

988 Q:
Which of the following is not one of the five most popular ice cream flavors: vanilla, chocolate, chocolate chip, butter pecan, strawberry, Neapolitan?

989 Q:
In 1858, a Philadelphia resident named H. L. Lipman was granted a patent for one of the most useful inventions in writing history. What was it?

990 Q:
In 1868, Wisconsin journalist Christopher Sholes received a patent for a machine he called a "Type-Writer." His invention had one major drawback. What was it?

991 Q:
Who was the first philosopher to use a typewriter?

992 Q:
In 2002, *TV Guide* magazine put out a list of the fifty top television shows of all time. What show was at the top of the all-time crop?

993 Q:
TV Guide also put out a list of the fifty worst shows of all time. What show was at the bottom of the heap?

988 A: Chocolate chip. It ranks sixth on the list. Rounding out the International Ice Cream Association's top ten list are French vanilla, cookies and cream, vanilla fudge ripple, and praline pecan.

989 A: The eraser-topped lead pencil. Lipman apparently had his eyes set squarely on the future: A few years after his pencil invention, he purchased the copyright for another historical breakthrough, the postcard.

990 A: Sholes's typewriter was a great innovation, but this all-capital contraption lacked a shift key. In 1878, the Remington Model 2 remedied that deficit.

991 A: Friedrich Nietzsche, who purchased his first typewriter in 1881. The great nihilist's attempts to master these primitive writing machines were very unsuccessful and frustrating. In fact, at least one commentator has suggested a connection between Nietzsche's frustration with typewriting and his insanity a few years later.

992 A: *Seinfeld.*

993 A: *The Jerry Springer Show.*

994 Q:
What other shows rounded out *TV Guide*'s five worst shows of all time?

995 Q:
What elective office did Jerry Springer hold before he became a TV star?

996 Q:
How long have cockroaches been on the planet?

997 Q:
Where can you find kangaroo rats?

998 Q:
When Great Britain's Queen Elizabeth was serenaded at her 2012 Diamond Jubilee concert by rock royalty, what new feature did she add to her attire?

999 Q:
What was the great *Doctor Who* purge? (Hint: It didn't happen on the show.)

994 A: *My Mother the Car* (1965–66), *XFL* (2001), *The Brady Bunch Hour* (1977), and *Hogan's Heroes* (1965–71).

995 A: In his better days, Springer was once the mayor of Cincinnati.

996 A: Cockroach fossils have been found that are over 250 million years old! And it is likely that cockroaches will still be around after human life no longer exists. Cockroaches adapt well to climatic changes, to say the least.

997 A: There are actually twenty-two species of kangaroo rats, which are small rodents found only in the more arid regions of western North America. They measure nine to fourteen inches in length, survive with very little water, come out only at night, and are named for their ability to leap with their hind legs and tail. Kangaroo rats live in shallow burrows, and they dig in the sand.

998 A: Earplugs. The long-serving monarch has never been fond of pop music.

999 A: Between 1972 and 1978, the BBC erased or otherwise destroyed more than two hundred early episodes of the now-classic show. To date, casts, crews, and fans have recovered most of them, but 106 episodes are still (sadly) missing.

1,000 Q:

How many species of insects exist on earth?

1,001 Q:

How many games did New York Mets pitchers go without a no-hitter? Who broke the spell?

1,000 A: Over one million—more species than all other animals combined. Several thousand new species are discovered each year. There are approximately 100,000 species of insects in North America alone.

1,001 A: When Johan Santana hurled his no-hitter on June 1, 2012, against the St. Louis Cardinals, it was the first no-hitter in the Mets' fifty-one-year franchise history. The thirty-three-year-old southpaw's feat came in the 8,020th game in team annals.